TENDING CRITTERS IN THE RIDGES

by

Clyde Brooks, DVM

Library of Congress Card Number: 2005908634

ISBN 978-0-9772881-0-6

First Printing July 2006
Second Printing March 2007

Book Cover – Clyde Brooks
Editor – Susan Snowden
Layout – Leonard Augie

Published by
Jabez Publications
101 Skyland Drive
Pisgah Forest, NC 28768
www.tendingcritters.com

Printed in the U.S.A. by
Morris Publishing
3212 East Highway 30
Kearney, Nebraska 68847
1-800-650-7888

A gift for Helen
from my friend Elena!
Just Because we
Love each other,
Glory to God!

To Linda, my wonderful wife, for providing continual encouragement and support, for being a loving mother to our three sons Keith, Wyatt and Travis, and for instilling excitement and fun into all the lives she touches.

CHAPTER ONE

Some things creep into our lives that we hardly notice. The crack in the living room wall that everyone but you sees. The little gray hairs that sneak their way into existence. And, while we are at it, the gradual receding hairline. You know what I mean. We think they have always been there when, in actuality, they haven't been. We have become accustomed to them. They don't get much, if any, attention anymore. Then there are those things that happen with such abruptness they can't be ignored. They demand your attention and interfere with your efforts to do anything else until they are properly addressed. Car wrecks, dirty diapers and the like fall into this category. It's the latter classification I'm addressing here. That abruptness came to me in the form of an eighty pound prolapsed uterus from a fourteen hundred pound Charolais cow. The cow had strained so forcefully in her labor to deliver her calf that she had literally turned her uterus inside out and pushed it through the vagina. My task would be to clean the contaminated organ and replace it in its proper position within the cow.

I didn't know it at the time, but the farm call I was about to make would be life changing. It would help me bring together a whole collection of free floating and yet undefined ideas I had about what lay ahead of me as a veterinarian. I was the junior member of a two-man veterinary practice on James Island, South Carolina. My wife, Linda, our three boys, and I had moved there immediately after I graduated from veterinary school, and I had been rapidly initiated into the world of veterinary practice.

The day had started like any other day. Kurt, the practice owner, and I had seen the usual mixture of cases from the routine examinations and heartworm treatments to the more demanding ones that involved gunshot wounds, the adjustment of insulin dosage for a diabetic cat, and the fracture repair on a dog that had been run over by a pizza delivery truck in the owner's driveway. Then just as I was on my way home, hopefully for a quiet evening, the car phone rang.

"Hello."

"Is this the 'vetnary'?"

"Yes, it is. How can I help you?"

"Well, this is Ben Hugot and I've got a cow with the calf bed out…need you right away."

"Where are you located Mr. Hugot?"

"In Dorchester. Two miles east of the US 78 and 15 junction. You'll see my name on the box."

I didn't have to look at the map to know that was a forty-mile drive and it was already seven P.M. "Mr. Hugot, you'll have to find someone else. It would take me an hour to get there."

"Don't matter none if you're two hours away. You're the only 'vetnary' that's answered my call and the cow is in a heap of trouble."

The conversation didn't advance much. The telephone signal was poor, to say the least, and there was no way I was going to persuade the farmer to find someone else. In reality, our practice was the only one within service range. Right after Mr. Hugot gave me directions to his farm, I pulled into a convenience store, topped off the gas tank, and bought two packages of cheese crackers and a Coke. I knew this would have to substitute for dinner tonight. I called Linda and told her what was happening and to expect me when she saw me.

I hadn't traveled ten miles when the phone rang again.

"Hello."

"Dr. Brooks, this is Warren Smithcoat in Orangeburg. My mule's got the colic something awful and needs tubing real bad."

The name wasn't familiar to me, but I felt the man knew a little about what treatment his mule needed by his use of the word 'tubing.' This was a common term used when a horse or mule was given mineral oil to move an irritant or blockage from the intestinal tract.

"Mr. Smithcoat, I'm on my way to another farm call in Dorchester and you're fifty miles past that. It sounds like your mule needs attention, but there is absolutely no way I can do it tonight. You'll have to transport your mule to Columbia to get the attention it needs."

Now, I won't go into Mr. Smithcoat's response. He was not happy and his language would not have pleased the FCC. I gave him directions for transport and hung up before he could unload again.

The drive to the Hugot farm was picturesque. Live oak trees were in a splendor with moss cascading gracefully over their limbs. Mile after mile mirrored the same vista. The trees were beautiful especially where the limbs draped over the road creating almost an arbor effect. But the same view was endless, and I felt an emptiness I couldn't identify. I fumbled for one of the cheese crackers and took a

2

bite. "Stale," I thought. Yes, that's it. Stale: The scenery is stale. Gorgeous though it was, it lacked variety. I was used to the north Georgia mountains and the variety of hills and hollows and mountain streams, tall white maples, lady slippers on a mountain path, and a change of seasons. My thoughts seemed to dwell on such things during the hour drive. Finally, I reached the turn to the Hugot farm. In the distance I saw a man frantically waving a large white towel over his head. I drove straight toward him.

He was wearing a peculiar sort of hat that I hadn't seen before. As I got closer, I could see it was a broad- rimmed straw hat with a mosquito net draped over it. He wore a long-sleeved dark shirt and his pants were tucked into rubber boots. I could barely make out his face but could see enough to know he had farmed for most of his sixty-plus years.

"What took you so long?" were the first words out his mouth.

I looked at the cow and was distressed at what I saw. Lying on her side and breathing rapidly, she was obviously on her way out without prompt attention. Mr. Hugot's brash greeting, 'What took you so long?' took on a whole new meaning. The uterus was huge and grotesquely swollen and covered with grass, mud, and an assortment of manure and small twigs. To the touch, the tissue was dry and brittle. Small areas of blood dotted the organ from where it had been dragged and even stepped on before the poor beast finally collapsed from exhaustion. Her left side was upward and seemingly ready to burst from the massive gas buildup in her rumen. The rumen is the second compartment in a cow's stomach. In this position the gas generated from the fermentation process that takes place in a cow's digestive tract was trapped with no place to go. Her newborn calf was trembling under a live oak tree about fifty feet away.

I called out a list of commands as I ran to the truck. "Mr. Hugot, go back to your house and call another man to help us, and bring me five gallons of clean water, five pounds of sugar, and a sheet. Do you have any cows that have calved in the last couple days?"

"Sure do."

"Great. Milk out a quart of colostrum and get another person to minister to that little calf over there."

As the farmer drove away, I quickly surveyed the order of events that must take place if this cow was to have a chance at survival. The bloat condition was rapidly claiming her life. I had to remedy that first and with minimal stress to the animal. I had learned only too painfully that tubing a cow in this condition was a textbook solution

3

that didn't work in real life. It took too long and caused panic in an already stressed-out animal. I reached in the equipment drawer and gathered a small surgical pack, cleaning solution, and a special instrument designed just for this type case… a trocar. A trocar is nothing more than a hollow tube with a cutting tip on one end. After a brisk cleaning of the skin over the bulging rumen, I made a one-inch incision through the skin and then plunged the trocar through the flank muscles and rumen wall. The methane gas released from the stomach erupted with such intensity that I had to hold the trocar forcefully in place to keep the instrument from dislodging. Once the pressure was released, I secured the trocar to the skin with sutures. This would prevent any further buildup of gas while I proceeded with the remainder of the treatment. The cow rose cautiously to a more normal resting position on her chest, and if a cow can smile like in the ads on TV, this cow would be one of those gifted ones with the contented look.

The easy work was over and so was the immediate threat of the cow dying. Next would come the painstaking process of cleaning the uterus and then replacing the organ back inside her. Whenever a uterus prolapses, it appears to double in size. It was like pouring ten gallons of water into a five-gallon container. The powerful arteries were still pumping blood into the organ while the veins had lost their ability to drain the surplus. Air exposure had dried the uterus and there was little to no muscle tone. Nothing could be done with the uterus at this point without the help of more manpower. A cow in this condition is low on calcium and would have to have a supplement to regain her strength. I went back to the truck and picked up a bottle of calcium solution and an intravenous administration set. The calcium would have to be given slowly to prevent heart problems. By that time, Mr. Hugot should have returned with help and we could get on to the task of replacing the uterus.

Once the solution was given, I expected to proceed directly to the clean-up and replacement work, but Mr. Hugot was nowhere to be found. It was 8:30 now and the mosquitoes and gnats had arrived in full force. In the distance was the sound of a tractor at full throttle. Mr. Hugot had pulled a trailer with him that had the five-gallon water container on it and two men hanging on for dear life as they bounced over the rough pasture.

He shut off the engine. "You got any idea how hard it is to find five pounds of sugar this time of night?"

"Never mind that. Did you get it?"

"Of course I did. You sent me out to get it, didn't you?"

"Great!" I said. "Back that trailer over here so the water is closer to and above the cow and give me the sheet. Who's got the colostrum?" He obliged as he demonstrated an uncanny ability to maneuver the attached trailer into the needed location.

Mr. Hugot eased himself from the tractor and put his hand on the shoulder of the man standing next to him. "This here is Jim from the next farm down the road and he's got the colostrum."

"See that calf over there, Jim?" I pointed to the tree. "The calf is hunkered down in there and is mighty weak. See if you can get it to nurse that bottle."

"Now this fine young man here is Bill Bob. I found him at the convenience store where I got the sugar and I hired him on the spot. I figured we was a'goin' need some muscle power."

"You're right", I said. We slid the sheet under the uterus and began the cleaning process. Mr. Hugot and Bill Bob suspended the uterus above the ground using the sheet as a sling as I poured water and soap across it.

"What was that?" I asked.

"What was what?" Hugot responded.

"It sounded like a thud...like something falling to the ground."

"I didn't hear anything. Besides, there's nothing to fall from except that tree over there where Jim and the calf are." Hugot said.

"O.K., lift the sheet a little higher so I can rotate this uterus a bit. O.K., that's good. Now, you can lower it a bit."

Even though I was wearing shoulder-length gloves, the whole process was still messy. The cow was in an upright position, resting on her chest, and I was in all sorts of contorted positions vigorously washing the uterus with soap and water. Finally, I had cleaned the uterus to my satisfaction and began to massage sugar into the organ's lining. The sugar would help pull the excess fluid from the uterine tissue and shrink its enormous size. Only then would I be able to push the uterus through the vaginal opening and put it back where it belonged. Replacing a uterus is a labor-extensive job. It is exhausting work. I had done the procedure many times and never had any doubt about my ability to successfully restore the organ to its proper position. However, tonight I had the elements working against me. The humidity had jumped at least ten points and the mosquitoes by a factor of ten. They were biting me on every exposed part of my body, and the gnats

5

were swarming in front of my face and in my eyes. I was envious of Mr. Hugot's hat.

"Lift the sheet a little higher. That'll help the blood flow back toward the body," I said as I stood briefly to relieve the discomfort in my back and knees. Then, I returned to the ground and continued the massage. Mercifully, the organ began to shrink and with ten more minutes of manipulation, the uterus slipped through the vagina and into its proper place within the abdomen. I grabbed two large antibiotic tablets, called boluses, and placed them in the uterus as I assured myself that the organ was fully distended and not partially folded on itself.

I ripped off my gloves, poured water over my head and rubbed frantically to relieve the itching sensation. The agony of my discomfort was lessened as I saw the cow struggle to her feet and stagger toward her calf. She completed the reunion with a cleaning swipe of her tongue to the calf's face.

"Don't want to do that anymore this time of night without a flashlight," Jim said.

"Why's that?" Mr. Hugot asked.

"Can't see the snakes."

"Snakes?" I said.

"That's right, snakes. There was a three-foot copperhead slithering down a limb when I pulled the calf from the bush. I didn't see him at first, but just sorta' got the feeling that something wasn't right. Then I saw him. I yelled out, but you fellows were so engrossed in what you were doing that you didn't hear me. Didn't have anything to defend myself so I just grabbed a stick, scooped it underneath him and flung him as far as I could. "

"In which direction?" I asked.

"Well, I didn't really have much time to aim, you know."

"Which direction, Jim?" I asked again.

"Pretty much over this way, I reckon." Jim replied.

"That explains the thud," I thought to myself. I figured where there was one snake there would be more, and poisonous snakes were not my favorite members of the animal kingdom. In a few minutes I had gathered all my instruments and supplies. The cow and her calf had reunited and my work was finished.

"Well Mr. Hugot, it's late and there's no reason to dally around here with a loose snake on the prowl. I'll just gather my things and be on my way. The office will send you a bill later this week." Within five minutes I was on my way. The ride home was very long or so it seemed. All I could think about was a shower and some kind of ointment that would give me relief from the hundreds of mosquito bites I had endured.

When I got home I gave Linda a quick kiss on the cheek and went straight for the shower. Linda brought a towel in to me.

"Is there anything I can do for you?" she asked.

"Yes, there is. Take the car this weekend and go to North Georgia and Western North Carolina and find us a home in the mountains."

"Are you serious?"

"I'll take care of the boys."

"All three?"

"Yes, all three."

"Really?" she said, knowing I must be desperate. "Throw in a shopping trip in Atlanta on the way and you've got yourself a deal."

As the hot water turned cold, I was shocked into reality about the hasty bargain I had just struck with Linda: three small boys, one still in diapers, for the entire weekend and my wife on an open-ended, unsupervised shopping trip in Atlanta. "What have I done?" I thought as I rushed from the bathroom with a towel wrapped around me. It was too late to withdraw the offer. Linda had already pulled out her suitcase and was making a list of needed additions to her limited wardrobe. Neither of us said anything, but we were both smiling at the prospect of moving back to the mountains.

CHAPTER TWO

Seven o'clock in the morning is too early to get up, especially when it is the second rising of the day. I had been up once already to encourage Linda on her way as she took to the roads leading to the north. I relinquished my Visa card with the understanding that the shopping trip in Atlanta was to be treated as a reward, a dessert you might say, and not the mission. Somehow, I didn't get the effect I wanted. She smiled, gave me a kiss, took the Visa card, and went on her way.

Travis was in the nursery, awake...ready to take on the new day. The older boys, Keith and Wyatt, were already eating the breakfast that Linda had somehow miraculously prepared before she left. That gave me time to change the baby's diaper and get dressed. It looked like it was going to be a good day - just dad and the boys. I was on call, but with a little bit of luck, we could have a good time. Linda and I had a philosophy on how to raise boys. First, keep them busy every waking second of the morning. Second, feed them and give them a nap. Third, keep them busy every waking second of the afternoon. Fourth, feed them, bathe them, read to them and put them to bed! That was my plan...no reason to deviate from it. It had always worked in the past, and it would work again today. We would walk to the pier, try our luck at fishing, have some lunch, walk back, and take a nap. In the afternoon we would do something else.

The fishing part went great. Keith caught his first fish ever, a puffer, one of those amazing fish that blows up to six times its original size when pulled from the water. We discussed it all the way home and pulled out the encyclopedia to look it up but could find nothing. Actually, we didn't have much time to search. Travis' dirty diaper took priority. How I had overlooked the certainty of this type of diaper change when I struck my deal with Linda escaped me. But I had done one of these before and knew I could do it again if I got everything in order and arranged in advance. I positioned the wash rag, powder, and fresh diaper on the floor and laid Travis next to them. I took off the diaper to discover that my sense of smell had deceived me. Things were worse than I had thought. It must have been the stewed prunes he ate for lunch. Just as I removed the diaper the emergency phone rang. Should I answer the phone or finish the task at hand? Not a big question most of the time.

"Travis, you just stay right there while daddy answers the phone." I backed toward the phone with my eyes on him as I lifted the receiver. "Hello."

"Dr. Brooks, this is Mrs. Fuller and I have a rather serious problem. Lady, our golden retriever, is in labor and can't deliver."

"How long has she been that way?" I said in horror as I saw Travis roll over toward the dirty diaper just a foot away from him. One more roll I thought and it's curtains.

"Well, let me think. It seems like it was before breakfast, but it could…"

"I need your answer quickly, Mrs. Fuller."

"You don't need to be so impatient, Dr. Brooks. It's been about eight hours."

Travis rolled over again and this time reached out for the dirty diaper.

"OH, NO!" I shouted.

Mrs. Fuller gasped, "Is it that serious?"

I dropped the phone, ran over to Travis, but it was too late. He had grabbed the diaper and pulled it over his hair and the left side of his face. I extracted the diaper from his tight little grip and dropped it on the floor. I went back to the phone. "What a hideous mess" were the first words from my mouth.

"Gee, doctor, I had no idea that eight hours in labor could cause such concern on your part. What should I do?"

"Meet me at the clinic in forty-five minutes," I said abruptly and hung up the phone.

The damage was done. There were dirty diaper contents everywhere…on the floor, on the telephone keyboard and headset, on me and, of course, all over Travis. I gathered the nerve to put my fingers on the numbers and called the emergency technician and told her to call one other technician and report to the clinic in half an hour for a possible C-section. Then, I called the babysitter on call to come over immediately to rescue me. I grabbed a wet cloth and began a quick decontamination of the disaster zone. I recruited Keith and Wyatt into action. Of course, they held their noses and made all kind of 'ug' and 'ou' sounds, but they were of some limited help. I washed Travis in the bathtub and then decked him out in a new outfit like nothing had happened. Keith and Wyatt entertained him while I changed clothes. My admiration for motherhood and especially Linda went up another whole level that afternoon. Mercifully, the babysitter arrived in short order and took charge of the boys. I gave her some quick instructions and then drove to the office.

Angie and Melissa, the two technicians, were busy preparing things just in case the emergency did develop into a cesarean section. Besides all the basic supplies needed for a routine surgery, a C-section had its own needs. They had assembled extra towels and sterilized clamps to clamp off the umbilical cords, and had warmed up the incubator to comfort the pups after delivery.

Mrs. Fuller arrived with Lady right behind her and barely able to walk. A quick examination revealed that Lady had some tissue hanging from her vaginal area. This was the afterbirth tissue that should still be protecting one of the pups in the womb. In labor four or more hours already, I was sure this first puppy was dead. I gently removed the placental tissue, cleaned the area and did a vaginal examination. There was no fetus in the birth canal and no palpable obstructions. I needed a radiograph before we could go any further. I asked the technicians to take an x-ray and to run calcium and glucose blood tests. While they did that, I explained the procedure to Mrs. Fuller.

"Mrs. Fuller, let me explain what we are doing. Lady can't deliver the pups for some explainable reason. Either she has a blockage of some sort or she is completely exhausted and can't continue with the labor. She may need a booster of calcium to help with her contractions or maybe just some glucose for energy. In any event, we will know what her needs are in just a few minutes."

About ten minutes later Angie popped the x-ray on the viewer.

"Aha," I said. "There's the problem."

"What is it?" Mrs. Fuller asked anxiously.

"The first pup is in a transverse position and has blocked the birth canal."

"What do you mean by a 'transverse' position?"

"Just as the pup slipped into the birth canal, it managed to turn sideways and is now trapped in a position that has halted the entire birthing process." Pointing to the location of the pup on the radiograph, I continued. "This pup can't get out and all the ones behind it can't either."

"What on earth can you do?"

10

"We'll have to perform a cesarean section and deliver the pups that way."

"Can't you just induce labor with a shot or something?"

"You're probably thinking of an oxytocin shot. Such a drug can be used in some deliveries but not when there's a blockage. The shot would cause strong contractions and since there is no way for the pups to get past the blockage, the contractions could cause a tear in the uterus that would endanger Lady's life. Besides, the calcium and glucose levels are low, so there is little likelihood that such a shot would be of any benefit even if we could use it."

"How many puppies are there?" Mrs. Fuller asked

"I can't tell for sure, but there are at least ten."

Mrs. Fuller placed her hand over her heart and looked heavenward. "Merciful heavens!" were the only words that fell from her lips.

After a brief pause, she inquired, "Do you charge by the pup? I mean, in human hospitals, there is a fee for one baby, more money for twins, even more for triplets. I can't imagine what it might be for …ten."

I took Mrs. Fuller by the hand and explained all that would take place while Angie and Melissa prepared Lady.

"No, we don't charge by the number of puppies we deliver," I explained, "And besides, there could very well be more than ten." I shouldn't have added that little parenthetical expression because she grabbed at her heart again. "I'll call you as soon as we complete the surgery." I escorted her to the door and made sure she was able to drive.

By the time I had changed into my scrubs, Angie and Melissa had shaved Lady's belly and established an IV catheter with fluids. Lady was quite weak, and I was concerned that the normal anesthetic regime might be too much for her. Besides, the standard injection we would normally give to start the anesthetic process would pass through the blood to the pups and depress them. So we opted to use only gas. We placed a mask over Lady's nose and mouth and gently held it in place while the anesthetic took the mother into a deep sleep.

Cesarean sections are generally straightforward but not without risk. First, I would make an incision through the skin and muscle and lift the uterus from the abdomen. Pulling the uterus from the abdomen had to be done with a delicate touch because a pregnant uterus is paper-thin and can tear just in the lifting process. Then I would make another incision into the uterus and deliver the pups. I would clamp off the umbilical cord and then hand the pup to the technicians. It's at this point that things get busy. The assistants would draw off fluid from the nose and mouth, rub the pup, and perhaps give an injection to stimulate breathing. They would then place the pup in the incubator and begin the process again with another pup. While doing all this, the assistants would have to continually tend to those pups already delivered to insure they were not in distress and institute any measures necessary to keep them alive.

I delivered the first pup -- the source of the problem. Just as the radiograph had revealed, the pup was lodged at the mouth of the birth canal. This was the one who had prematurely expulsed its placenta. It was dead, of course. I removed it and methodically began to deliver pup after pup after pup.

I handed the last pup to Angie. "How many is that?"

"Seventeen and all are doing well except for the very first one!" she said with an exhausted smile on her face.

I closed the incision in a routine manner and tended to Lady's recovery while the techs continued their care for the newborns. In short order Lady was awake and looking around nervously. She knew something had happened but wasn't sure what. We presented the puppies to her and she busied herself with cleaning and nursing her new litter.

The next order of the day was the telephone call to the owner. "Good news, Mrs. Fuller. Lady is doing just great and so are all of her pups."

"I'm so relieved. How many were there?"

"Oh…there were…quite a few," I said with a guarded voice.

"How many is quite a few?"

"Well, there were…there were…actually, the count came to sixteen."

"SIXTEEN!"

"And they are all healthy," I said defensibly.

There was a long pause.

"What ever am I going to do?"

"Fortunately, Lady will do most of the work. However, there are some things you will have to do. Come down and we'll go over all that with you."

Just as I was putting down the receiver, my beeper went off again. I called the number and Tad Kender, caretaker for the cats at Charles Towne Landing, the local zoo, answered. "Thanks for calling,

Dr. Brooks. Carolina, our mountain lion, has a large laceration on her left front arm and needs attention right away."

Angie and Melissa had everything well in hand. We discussed what to tell Mrs. Fuller and how to ease her into the reality that she had come to the clinic earlier that afternoon with one dog and was leaving with seventeen. I left to tend to Carolina.

The cat habitat was well designed. The lions lived in a natural outdoors setting that was separated from the public by a steep embankment guarded by an electric wire and a water barrier. At one end of the habitat was a funnel-type enclosure where the cats came to feed at the end of the day. The animal caretakers could observe the cats closely in this setting. Tad was dropping the food through the feeding trough when he first saw the laceration. The wound extended from the elbow to the upper part of the paw…about ten inches long. There was no bone exposure.

"Any idea what caused that?" I asked Tad.

"Not yet. I've sent a couple men in there now that the habitat's empty to see if we can figure it out."

"We'll have to sedate her to suture that wound."

"How are you going to do that?"

"I'm trying to figure that out myself. One hundred pounds of angry cat can really do a job on a person if he's not careful." The enclosure had a narrow spot in it. "Tad, if you can entice Carolina into the forward part of the enclosure I think I can just reach her rear leg and inject an anesthetic. What do you think?"

"I don't know, Doc. That may be a little risky. She's powerful and mighty fast. If you are slow with the needle, you may go in with an arm and come out with a nub."

"Let's give it a go." I drew up the anesthetic. "Tad, distract her with that slab of meat."

Tad dropped a five-pound slab of raw meat into the cage and Carolina moved forward to get it. She dropped down and pulled the meat toward her and then tore into it with a ferocity that made me temporarily question my plan. She gazed at me and let out a hiss that exposed her inch and half long canine teeth. Then she turned back to the meat and was momentarily distracted. Her leg was about ten inches from the edge of the cage. This was the moment. With a rapid and deliberate motion, I reached through the bars and injected her in the thigh. She spun around with a paw that looked to be the size of a saber tooth tiger's and slammed it into the bar, barely missing my hand. The meat flew through the air and splattered all of us.

"That was close," I said as I wiped the sweat and meat splatters from my brow.

"I told you she was fast."

In about ten minutes the full affect of the anesthetic was evident and we entered the enclosure. The wound was perhaps four hours old and there was swelling throughout the injured area. I would have to trim away some of the severely damaged skin, and I knew that even the small amount of skin that I had to remove would make complete closure of the laceration impossible. We cleaned the wound, trimmed as little skin as possible, and closed about ninety percent of the area. The lower, unclosed portion would act as an area for drainage. As Carolina was recovering we discussed antibiotic treatment and what to watch for during the healing process. The sutures would absorb in about thirty days so we wouldn't have to go through the anesthetic ordeal to remove them.

"See you later, Tad. Give me a call if you have any questions." With that I left to go home. Hungry and exhausted, I arrived around 7:30. At least the boys would be bathed and fed and I could relax a little. The baby sitter met me at the door.

"We had a great time while you were gone," she said. "We played games, went on a walk and did all sorts of things. In fact, we had so much fun, I lost tract of time and haven't fed them supper yet."

"But, they are bathed, aren't they?"

"Bathed? Was I supposed to bathe them?"

Try as I might, I was unable to bribe the sitter into helping me with the baths and dinner. She had a date and was already late. I was filthy after my dealings at the zoo and certainly couldn't wash the boys until I had cleaned myself. Travis was too small and the other boys too young to leave them unattended while I took a shower so I did the only logical thing. I picked up all three boys and we jumped into the bath together. Dinner was a quick PB & J with milk. Afterwards, we all fell into bed. As my thoughts faded toward sleep, I distinctly remembered passing the church on the way home and seeing the title for tomorrow's message. Funny how it took on a whole new meaning. The message was from the fifth chapter of Ephesians titled "Husbands, Love Your Wife." Linda would be home tomorrow and with that good thought on my mind, I faded into unconsciousness.

CHAPTER THREE

It was Monday morning and I was back in the security of my office where I felt reasonably confident that I could handle most of what would come my way ...big change from the weekend. Linda had returned late last night with the good news that she had found a location that was just perfect. Too tired to go into the details, she promised to organize the information by the end of today. She must have been really tired because she didn't notice the two bouquets of flowers I had bought her or even the nice clean house. I had hired Good Friday's Maid Service to straighten things up a bit – not that the house really needed it - and even at double time rates because of the weekend, it was worth every penny.

The telephone rang. It was Bill Moyer, the ranger at Bulls Island.

"Good morning, Bill...Oh, no! Really? I'm so sorry to hear that...Any ideas what happened?...Sure, bring in her body and we'll see if we can figure it out...What's that?...Right, see you around noon."

"What was all that about?" Angie inquired.

"That was the Ranger overseeing the Red Wolf Project. He found the female wolf dead this morning and doesn't have a clue what killed her. No wounds, no apparent hemorrhage. Just cold stone dead. He's bringing her here for necropsy to see if we can find the cause of death. He has already notified the federal authorities, and they gave him the okay to pursue the cause of death. This will really throw a kink in their project."

The red wolf is a relatively solitary animal that once roamed throughout the southeastern United States. Aggressive predator control programs and habitat changes due to the encroachment of human settlements had reduced the entire population of these animals to less than a few hundred. In the early '70s, the U.S. Fish and Wildlife Service initiated the Red Wolf Project in an effort to prevent extinction of the species. They captured approximately fourteen red wolves and transported them to Point Defiance Zoo in Tacoma, Washington. Matched breeding pairs were then relocated to five different habitats in

North and South Carolina. The habitat in our area was located on Bulls Island just north of Charleston. Since our practice was the consulting practice for the local zoo, the U.S. Fish and Wildlife Service felt we were the natural choice to act as the consulting veterinarians for their project.

As I gathered the instruments needed for the necropsy, I began thinking about the last visit I made to the island. "Angie, could you get the write-up on the last trip to Bulls Island?"

She handed me the notebook. The last entry was six weeks ago. The ranger had called me with some concern that the female was acting strange and wanted me to observe her. I loved getting these calls because it meant a full day excursion to a beautiful coastal island. The trip made me feel like Marlin Perkins from my early TV viewing days. Just getting there was an adventure. Bill had a fourteen-foot fishing boat with a ten horsepower outdoor engine to transport us to the island. We clipped along at a good speed through the choppy water and were there in about twenty minutes. Then we hopped in a jeep and drove about a half mile over a dirt road to the enclosed habitat.

Bulls Island is a twenty-two mile barrier island located in the Cape Romain National Wildlife Refuge. The island is a rugged but beautiful place and was the perfect location for such a project. Besides its recently acquired occupants, it was a bird sanctuary and the home for other creatures such as deer, cottonmouth moccasins and, you guessed it, alligators. The wolves had originally been allowed to roam the thousand-acre wild life refuge without restraint. They had telemetry collars so they could be easily located as the study of their habits dictated. The wolves didn't like the arrangement but could not escape the accommodations because of the long swim to the mainland. One day, however, on the eve of a full moon, the tide had been exceedingly low. The wolves seized the moment and swam off the island in the quest for freedom. A helicopter pursuit and tranquilizer guns were needed to convince them they couldn't do that. To prevent similar problems in the future, the Wildlife Service constructed a one-hundred foot diameter enclosure with a ten-foot high chain-linked fence to contain the wolves.

Wild animals panic very easily when captured. They can become so stressed that they will literally die from a condition called, for lack of a better name, stress induced death. We decided we would first observe them from a distance to see if we could determine anything obvious. If we failed in this effort, we would have to enter the fenced-in area and capture the wolf for examination. I wanted to avoid this if possible because of possible risk to both the wolf and to us. We located ourselves behind a palmetto tree about two hundred feet from the enclosure. We were on the upwind side so the wolves could not pick up our scent. "Perfect," I thought. "Neither wolf had detected our presence." I pulled out the binoculars and watched the wolves for a while. The male was paying very close attention to the female and periodically made an advance toward her that would be rebuked with a snarl.

"How long you noticed this, Bill?"

"First saw it four days ago… on Monday. She's not so agitated today. Seems to be a little more tolerant of the male. At first, I thought they had been fighting because I saw one or two drops of blood in the feeding area."

"Is she eating her normal ration?"

"No changes there," he replied.

I focused the binoculars on the female. "I believe I see the problem…yes, I'm sure of it. She's in heat."

"In heat? Is that all it is? How can you tell?"

"She has an off-white vaginal discharge and the vulva is swollen about three times normal size. Add that to the male's attentive behavior and her gradual tolerance of his attention over the last four days and that would explain it. That would also explain the small amount of blood you saw. In the first stage of heat, the vaginal discharge is blood tinged. We could go in if you like, but I'm about ninety-five percent sure it's just a hormonal thing."

Bill concurred that we didn't need to stress the wolves any further. We packed up and then returned to the boat. When I got back to the office, I jotted my findings in the notebook.

I was jolted from my thoughts when Angie came in the room. "The zoo just brought in a pelican that was attacked by a raccoon. Have we got time to fix it before the wolf arrives?"

"Blasted", I thought. It wasn't that I didn't like pelicans…it was their smell. Their pouch reeked of spoiled fish. It was tough working on them just because of the odor. Kurt had once remarked "The stench is enough to gag a maggot." We had even jokingly made a policy that all sterile surgery on pelicans would be performed in the outdoor area behind the clinic. Just last week, we had to do a partial amputation of a pelican's foot from another raccoon attack. It took us three days and every odor elimination product we could find just to remove the smell from the clinic.

"You'll love this one. He has a torn pouch", Angie said.

A torn pouch. That would mean an intimate closeness with the bird's beak and the source of its odor.

"Okay, bring it into the laceration room, and we'll try to confine the odor to that area. Turn every exhaust fan on. Maybe, that will help."

"It won't help, but I will switch them on. We tried that last time," Angie reminded me.

The two-inch bite wound was relatively fresh and wouldn't be difficult to close. We positioned the tracheal tube down the bird's windpipe, initiated the anesthetic gas and cleaned the wound.

"Wait a minute. I've got an idea! Position that room fan behind me and direct it over my shoulder. That way the odor won't be right in my face. Why didn't I think of that last time?"

"Are you sure you want to do that?" Angie replied.

"Of course, I am. Just get it and turn it on high. I want to get this finished in due haste."

Dutifully, Angie did exactly as I had so hastily directed. She placed the fan behind me, directed over my right shoulder and turned the switch to high. There was a little detail I had overlooked. This pelican had been traumatized by a raccoon, which had ruffled and, shall we say, 'loosened' a whole parcel of feathers.

"Cut it off, cut it off!"

It was too late. As the fan reached full speed, I could see the disaster unfolding. In short order, the entire room was full of feathers. The room was raining feathers, parts of feathers and other loose debris from the bird's body. Angie was laughing.

"That's not funny!"

She couldn't contain herself. "You've got feathers in your surgical mask, your hair…why there's even some on your eyebrows."

I waived the feathers away from my face and continued to suture the wound while Angie went for the vacuum cleaner. To make a long story short, we completed the minor surgery, recovered the pelican from anesthesia and cleaned up most the mess, save a few floating feathers, just before Bill arrived.

"I want to see the creature you just finished. Anything that smells like a fish and wears feathers must be something unique", Bill said as he covered his nose with a handkerchief.

"Very funny. We just had one of our daily disasters. Nothing really", I replied.

"Gosh, that odor's awful. Smells like a fish died in here last week while the air conditioner was off. What are the chances we can do this necropsy in another room?" Bill asked.

We set up our instruments in an adjoining exam room while Bill went to his truck to retrieve the dead wolf.

Bill's demeanor changed as he placed the wolf on the table. "This is not a fun part of either of our jobs", he said.

"You're right, Bill. Well, let's get started."

A necropsy is the term used for a postmortem on an animal, and there is no polite way to describe the procedure. One has to examine every organ in an effort to find the cause of death, and that is done only with dissection. Even though I suspected the cause of death, I went through the process in a very methodical way. But there were no surprises. The cause of death was right there in front of me when I opened the abdomen.

"Bill, do you remember the last time you called me to Bull's Island and I told you the female was in heat?"

"Yes, why?"

"That heat cycle didn't proceed as it should have. Something got out of whack and messed up the reproductive hormones. Her uterus is full of pus. She died of an infected uterus…what we call a pyometra. We see a few cases of this same sort of thing each year in dogs. It's difficult for the owner to even know anything is wrong. The condition sets in very gradually over a four to six week period until finally the dog becomes sick enough for the owner to pick up on it. A wild animal covers up its sickness as a protective defense. I don't see any way in the world you could have detected this."

"What's the treatment?"

"In pets, we just spay them and remove the infected organ. Of course, with the wolf, that would have ended the research on this pair."

"What do you think caused this to happen?"

"Difficult to say for sure. Probably the stress of a new environment, the artificial nature of an enclosure and probably many other things. No way of knowing for sure."

"Well, this sure does throw a monkey wrench into the study. Mind if I use your phone? I need to call the biologist in Tacoma."

Just as a matter of record, Angie and I finished the necropsy by taking samples and bacterial cultures from all the organs. We packaged those along with some stomach and intestinal fluid samples and readied them for submission to the pathology lab.

Bill came back into the room. "The long and short is this: We prepare the male for shipment back to the zoo where they will try to match him with another female. When that happens, they will ship the pair back here and we start over."

"Gee, I'm sorry, Bill."

"It's not a great set back. We expected some things not to go just as planned. We're venturing into new territory here, so we can expect some delays along the way."

"Well, I know you're disappointed. You've put so much work into the project. Let me know if there is anything I can do. In the meantime, I'll notify you as soon as we hear from the pathologist on these samples."

No sooner had Bill left than Angie came back to the room. "Guess what?"

"No telling," was the only reply I could muster.

"It seems the pelican wasn't just on the receiving end of the altercation. The zookeeper found the raccoon and it has a tooth hanging from its mouth. They want you to examine it, pull any teeth needing extraction and, in general, fix it up so they can return it to the habitat. I told them you would love to fix up the little fellow."

CHAPTER FOUR

The day had been so hectic that I hadn't even touched base with Linda. Angie poked her head in my office door. "It's Linda on line one."

"Hi, honey. We must be on the same wavelength. Sorry I haven't called you today."

"That's okay. Angie brought me up-to-date on the type of day you had. I just wanted you to know how excited I am about what I saw, and I just can't wait to tell you. But first, I want to thank you for the daisies you gave me and also the roses are absolutely beautiful."

"I'm glad you like them."

"Tell me, Clyde, how in the world did you have time to take the boys fishing and handle all the emergencies you had."

"Well ..."

"And the house? It's spotless!"

"Well ..."

"Never mind, that's not important. What is important though is our date tonight. You're not on call, I've hired a baby sitter, and we're going to Hymans so I can tell you what I found on my trip."

We had a terrific dinner. Hymans was noted for its excellent lobster. Linda was so excited with all she had to tell me that she did not savor the lobster in her customary manner. She used the nutcrackers on the claws like a weapon and proceeded in a very efficient fashion to finish off the entire lobster in short order.

My baked potato was still steaming when she said, "Okay, are you ready?" She placed the claw crackers on the table and reached across the table and grabbed my hand in both of hers. "Let me tell you what I saw. It is the most gorgeous sight I've ever seen, and guess what? They need another veterinarian. The city's name is Brevard and it is located in the Blue Ridge Mountains of North Carolina, and the people there are wonderful. The area has so many waterfalls you can't count them, then there are..." Her beautiful brown eyes were wide open with excitement as she continued her detailed descriptions over the next hour.

Timing could not have been better. A new replacement for me would be easy since it was June and new graduates with veterinary diplomas in hand would be seeking jobs. Kurt understood my desire to return to the mountains and gave me his best wishes. He agreed that a month would be plenty of time to seek my replacement. In the meantime, I would continue with my normal duties.

The next month was a whirlwind experience. Too many details to note but suffice it to say we investigated the schools and churches in the area and talked to bankers, real estate agents, pediatricians, farmers, agricultural agents and, of course, we checked out the local grocery stores. We liked what we saw and knew Brevard would be where we would settle our family roots. We established Mountain View Veterinary Hospital in September 1977 and thanked God for his provision in directing us to our new home.

The move had not been easy. Three days before we were to leave Charleston, Linda had a wreck in our only vehicle. Fortunately, the boys were not in the car and she escaped without injury, but the car was totaled. We negotiated a deal for a station wagon and moved on schedule. We came to Brevard with only one thousand dollars in our pockets. On one of our preliminary visits, we had secured a rental house and found a bank that had agreed to extend us credit while we established the practice. But those first few years were difficult and more than once we wondered if we would survive the economic hardship of supporting a family and establishing a veterinary practice at the same time. Our commitment was to prevail. We knew the move would be arduous and tax our resources, but we felt confident that we could firmly establish ourselves and the veterinary practice into this wonderful community.

A small community is special. In a large city, there are often times so many conflicts to overcome that some of the really neat things in life get lost in the scramble. For instance, we have a high school home coming parade right down the middle of town. Everything stops for two or three hours while the band, homecoming queen and her court in convertibles, athletes, a host of special vehicles, such as fire trucks and EMS vans parade through the down town streets. Then a couple months later we do it again for Christmas. But this time there will also be some horses with riders in full cowboy costume.

Over our first few years in Brevard, we learned that the streets in the downtown area are often closed to celebrate special holidays. And sometimes they are closed just to celebrate life. In the summer,

East Main Street is closed every Tuesday night for a street square dance. The musicians are in the gazebo and the dancers on the street. From the very first year in Brevard, we immersed ourselves in the local activities. We acted as youth leaders for the church, pack leaders for cub scouts, summer camp coordinators for the local Rotary Club high school camp, coached youth basketball and participated in a host of other things. The first few years had passed like a whirlwind. But here we were…exactly where we wanted to be while raising our three boys. These thoughts were coming to mind now, as our family gathered around the table. Linda looked at me as if she read my thoughts and squeezed my hand as she whispered, "We made the right choice, honey. Just look how happy the boys are." And then, as if it were a planned finale to this moment, Travis, with his older brothers, Keith and Wyatt cheering him on, blew out the seven candles in one exhausted breath. Linda and I looked at each other again knowing how fortunate we had been in our six short years in Brevard.

Emergencies are no respecter of weekends, time of day, birthday parties or anything else for that matter, and I was reminded of that when my pager beeped. The call was from Clarence Owenby. His only cow, Rosie, was down and he needed help right away.

The ride to Clarence's farm was just a short drive down highway 276. A branch of the French Broad River was to my right and the mountains that dropped to the highway framed the left side of the road. March is a transitional month with little to anything in bloom. But there are small buds on the trees and there was the anticipation that in another month, spring would arrive in all its splendor. I wanted to keep that thought in mind because this past winter had been bitter. I turned left onto a dirt road that led to the farm and parked just in front of a functional though dilapidated barn. The color of the barn was probably once a vibrant red. Now, it was just a mixture of a chipped and faded rouge color intermixed with assorted planks to close the large holes where time had taken its toil. Primer had been added in random places in an effort to extend the structure's life. Clarence was sitting on a stool just inside the barn and was gently stroking the cow's forehead. It was easy to see there was some special bond between them. Neither had noticed my arrival.

Clarence Owenby was one of the finest men you would ever want to meet. He wasn't much to look at physically. Arthritis had crippled him over the years and left him humpback at the shoulders and dependent on a black locust walking cane. He had a stiff neck and faced mostly toward the ground due to an infirmity in his back. He didn't have long wavy hair or even a bald scalp like so many men his age. Instead, he sported a short-cropped crew cut, which his wife devotedly gave him once each month. And he wore blue jean overalls with a long sleeved white shirt. He looked his seventy-six years.

Clarence had farmed all his life, mostly vegetables, but he also maintained a few livestock. All that was behind him now except for one small jersey milk cow named Rosie. As I talked to Clarence, it became quite evident he had a severe hearing impairment. In fact, the only way I could communicate with him was to yell into his left ear from a distance not exceeding four inches…his right ear was totally useless.

"She mostly gives a gallon ev'ry milking, Doc, but lately she doing right smart to come up with even a quart. I wouldn't have bothered you none, but all my remedies haven't help her along much."

Rosie did appear unthrifty. She didn't seem to be in any real discomfort but her big, brown eyes lacked the clear luster present in a healthy cow and her hair coat was dull. Her temperature was normal, but the old gentleman told me she was not eating her usual amount.

Cows are peculiar creatures when it comes to their digestive system. They have what some people call 'four stomachs'. Actually, the stomach has four distinct compartments. The first two, the reticulum and the rumen, are fixed anatomically in position while the last two, the omasum and abomasum, are more movable. Rosie had the symptoms of a displaced abomasum. The abomasum is the fourth compartment and had probably slipped to a position where it shouldn't be. It was, more or less, trapped in an abnormal location and unable to properly function.

I put on a shoulder length glove and prepared to do a rectal examination. There is a world of information available from this type exam, but it is messy. In fact, the only limitations are in the length of the arm and the obliging nature of the cow. I inserted my arm into the rectum of the cow and began to feel the recognizable structures through the rectal lining. Nothing is felt directly. That is, I could feel Rosie's bladder, ovaries, and other structures indirectly through the rectum. It is somewhat like feeling an object while wearing a cotton garden glove as compared to the bare hand. My fingers had to be my eyes as they searched through a maze of familiar anatomy. I worked my way toward her lower right side and pressed upward. Something didn't feel right and my suspicion was growing. I took off my glove, grabbed my stethoscope, and went to her left side.With the stethoscope in place on Rosie's lower left side, I thumped the area with my thumb and middle finger. There was a distinct 'pinging' sound from trapped gas. The abomasum had slipped under the giant rumen and was trapped. This compromised the organ's function in that normal stomach fluid and gas were partially impeded from exiting. "Clarence, I'm, afraid we have a rather serious problem."

"You'll have to speak a little louder, young man."

Of course. I was a good five feet away and communication distance was, at best, half a foot. "Sorry, Clarence." I maneuvered toward his left ear. "I said we have a rather serious problem."

"What's that?" he yelled back.

"It's her stomach. It's moved to an abnormal position and is causing her some problems."

"Well, put it back where it ought to be."

"It's not quite that simple. She will require surgery."

He twisted his head a little closer. "Require what?"

"Surgery. That is about the only chance we have to correct her problem."

Clarence took the weight off his walking stick and held it straight out as if he were pointing to a far off object. His head crept into alignment. His thoughts seemed to be in another place and time, and then he quipped, "She too old for that." He lowered his cane and shifted his weight to relieve the momentary stress he had place on his crippled frame. "I mean she does have a stomach and it's a good one, I take, just a little out of place. Might there not be something else we can do?"

Sometimes there are just no good alternatives and this was one of them. Clarence was right. Rosie had to be at least fifteen years old and such a surgery would be hard on her. I thought for a moment. "There is a way that sometimes works. We can put her in a trailer and carry her across that bumpy stretch of pasture over there to the south of your house. Sometimes such a ride will jostle the insides around enough to put things back in place."

There was a twinkle in Mr. Owenby's eyes as he headed straight for the tractor and trailer. We encouraged Rosie up the ramp and onto the two-wheeled hay wagon. Clarence may have had arthritis and a neck that wouldn't stand at attention, but that didn't slow him down a bit. He amazed me with his driving agility. After all, his head was facing ninety degrees away from his direction of travel.

He returned in about fifteen minutes. I really didn't expect much and had suggested the effort only to give Clarence a little hope and to help him come to grips with the serious problem we were facing. I put on another glove and reexamined Rosie. To my amazement the abomasum had moved. There was not a complete correction but some adjustment had taken place. Again there was a sparkle in Clarence's eyes as he saw a smile spread across my face.

"Well, we made some progress. Her stomach is more toward where it should be after that ride. She should do fine, but you can't use her as a breeding cow anymore. She's not a hundred percent, and a pregnancy would surely be against her."

"That'll be all right. She's too old for that anymore anyway. Just as long as she'll be okay." Clarence seemed to stand a little taller as he walked now. He and Rosie had been together a long time and he felt good about her recovery.

As I got into my truck, I saw a bull about a hundred yards away on the other side of the river. Clarence read my thoughts. "You needn't worry about him none, Doc. He's as old as me and lost interest. Even if he had a mind to, he'd probably drown in the crossing."

I was too hoarse to say good-bye or carry on more conversation so I just waved to Clarence out the truck window as I drove away. As I turned on the main road, I caught a glimpse of the bull in my rearview mirror. Through the reflection of the mirror I saw him raise his head and stare straight at me. It was like I was in the twilight zone. An eerie sensation penetrated down my spine. I would not realize what my instincts were telling me for another six months.

The birthday party had moved outside and the boys were playing stickball. The terrain of the playing field was such that the batter was down hill from the pitcher. No one liked to play catcher because any misses meant running down hill to retrieve the ball. The boys, as they had done before, recruited Hops, our three-legged, black poodle, as catcher. It was really something. There was Hops behind the batter just like he had studied his position. Of course, Hops missed every ball that got past the batter. But he just swiveled on his stump leg and retrieved the ball and then carried it to the pitcher. He played catcher for both sides and the boys loved it.

Most vets have at least one handicapped pet. Our family was no exception. Hops had come to us by accident. A year earlier, a man had brought him to the clinic. This man was rude, crude and otherwise unkempt. He had no social skills and had made no attempt to be polite as he barged into the exam room.

"How much to fix this dog?" he said as he grabbed the dog by the nap of his neck and jerked him onto the exam table. The dog winced in pain as he struck the table. Dried, crusted blood covered the poor animal.

"Careful", I said, "That dog's in a lot of pain"

"Pain? He don't know pain. He caused me a heap of trouble. Just wait 'til I get him home."

"His right rear leg is dangling and is almost severed. What happened to him?"

"He was in the driveway when I got home and wouldn't move so I thought I teach him a lesson. He'd see. The blasted dog just lay there and got hit. It was his fault, stupid dog."

"What's his name?"

"Never got around to giving him one. He's worthless anyway. We just call him dog."

"Your dog is in terrible shape. In addition to the obvious serious injuries, he's anemic and undernourished."

"Don't give me all the details…just tell me what it'll cost to fix him."

"I'll put together an estimate for you."

"Let's just cut to the end. If it's goin' be more than twenty-five dollars you can just knock him in the head and put him out of his misery." The complete disregard for the welfare of this poor creature was, to me, totally incomprehensible.

"Sir, I can assure you the cost to amputate a leg, and that is what we will have to do, will exceed your twenty-five dollar limit." I stared him straight in the eyes and I saw only evil for this dog of his.

"Just keep him and put him down or do whatever you want with him. I never had a dog worth more than the bag of food I feed him. And this one is sure at the bottom of the list of all the ones I've had." With that he turned around and stomped out the door.

There was no choice for the right rear leg. It had been crushed beyond repair and was almost severed. That wasn't what concerned me. It was the other rear leg. The deep gash in it had exposed the thigh bone, and the contamination was terrible. If, after amputation of the right rear leg, the other leg became infected, the dog would have gone through the entire ordeal for nothing and would have to be euthanized. I decided to proceed one step at a time and count on the healing power God had instilled in all his creatures to carry us through.

The surgery went fine and the left leg healed without complication. A few weeks of convalescence, treatment for intestinal parasites, good groceries and the tender loving care of the boys brought this little creature back to life. Next, we had to decide on a name. All

27

the neighborhood children got together and decided that this little dog needed a special name. After all, he had gone through so much. A name like Butch or Pepper just wouldn't do considering his ordeal. So, they held a special ceremony and knighted him. He would be known as Sir Hops-A-Lot, but it would be okay if we called him Hops for short.

And that is how we came about this fine little gentleman of a dog. He had come a long way since that fateful day when the dreadful man brought him to me. I could only laugh now as I saw the pitcher wind up and deliver the pitch...the batter swung and missed...and Hops wagged his tail as he chased the ball down the hill.

CHAPTER FIVE

The next morning was routine. Susan, the receptionist, had done an excellent job of scheduling the appointments, and for once there were no surprises to stir up the schedule. Fortune had shined on me when I had hired Susan right after opening the practice. I had advertised in The Transylvania Times that I was looking for someone who could function as both a receptionist and a veterinary technician. At that early stage of practice, I was on farm calls a fair percentage of time and needed someone who could be efficient in scheduling both small animal office appointments and large animal calls that required travel time to and from the calls. Susan came to the rescue and brought with her an inordinate organizational ability. Packed in her five-foot four inch frame was an administrative talent that I have seen only a couple times in my life. Susan was a native of the county and knew the roads like the back of her hand. She could give me directions to farms to expedite my travel. And she knew the people. She knew the personalities of the people, the makeup of the families and in short almost everything I needed when making a first call to a client. When I was in the office, she was an exceptional surgical assistant and very capable with the microscope and lab equipment. Her greatest gift, however, was her compassion. She was a true asset and I was indeed fortunate to have her in the practice. This morning she had moved the schedule around a bit so that I could get to the barbershop before the lunchtime crowd. With a little luck I could run down to the barbershop, get a quick buzz and catch lunch.

The Main Street Barber Shop was usually busy at lunchtime, but today I had beat the crowd. Just as I was opening the door, someone called to me.

"Hold on, Doc. Just a minute, please". It was Arnold McCall and two of his friends. I recognized one as Bill Larenby, but the other one I didn't know. "We've got a quick question for you."

"I was just on my way to get a hair cut," I said as another man slipped between me and the door and then straight into the barber's chair.

"Ah, this won't take no time, Doc. We got a problem with a steer and need your input," Bill said.

"Last fall, the three of us here went in together and bought a steer. We never done nothin' like that before, and well, we didn't exactly make the right preparations, you know." It was obvious Arnold was a bit embarrassed. He moved a little closer so people walking along the sidewalk wouldn't overhear. "Now, we can't catch him."

"Can't catch him?"

Arnold looked to his left and right to see if anyone had heard my comment. Then in almost a whisper, "It's this way, Doc. We made up this little...Jay, why don't you just tell him. You know the details better anyway."

Jay slipped in close and took Arnold's place. "We thought it would be like shooting fish in a barrel, easier than falling off a log, quicker than a cat's meow, as simple as one...two...three, as easy as pie, a piece of cake..." Jay went on increasingly. Meanwhile two more people had entered the barbershop.

"I think I've got the idea."

"Oh, for Pete's sake, Jay! You'd go across town and make a U-turn to get to the house next door. Can't you see the man needs to get in the barbershop and there you are just a'goin' on and on. Just let me do the details." Arnold was obviously annoyed. He pulled me out of hearing distance of Jay. "You know Jay is his given name, but everyone around these parts calls him CJ. That's short for Cliché Jay."

"Cliché Jay?" I said with only a little puzzlement.

"Yea, that's right. Cliché Jay. Others call him Chatter Jay. The boy don't always talk that way but when he does...well, it's enough to drive a good man crazy. He don't mean any harm with it and he's not acting cute. He just gets nervous and you see what happens. I sometimes think that red kinky hair of his just gets wound up in a knot and puts pressure on his brain."

In addition to Jay's red hair, he had an old western type handle bar mustache that dominated his face. It accentuated his long rectangular face and closely set, almost beaded, eyes. His wiry six-foot one inch frame would support the old saying, as Jay would put it, 'no moss would grow under his feet.'

I peered around Arnold's huge frame and saw two more men enter the shop. The opportunity to get a quick haircut was fading fast. Arnold edged me back toward the other two.

"Here's what we were thinking."

"The long and short of it, you might say," Jay interjected.

30

"Right." Arnold continued. "We need a tranquilizer of some sort to slow Wooley down."

"You named the steer you'll be roasting on the grill?"

"That's all CJ's fault. He thought the steer should have some name rather than us always just referring to him as 'that steer'. The hair coat on that steer was kinda' like a wool coat and CJ up and called him 'Wooley' one day, and well… the name stuck. We're sorry we done it now, 'cause it's going to be hard to do him in when the time comes since he's got a name and all. Anyway, we need a tranquilizer."

"I thought you couldn't catch him."

"Can't." Arnold said. "That's where CJ comes in. He's good with a bow. Once got a merit badge in archery when a boy scout."

"You're going shoot him with an arrow?"

"That's why we need the tranquilizer. We've rigged up a special arrow. The metal tip has been replaced with a syringe and needle that will stick in Wooley. When the medicine takes effect, we'll move in and catch him. CJ, go to the pickup and fetch that arrow you made."

"Back in a flash," Jay said as he darted up the hill to the truck.

Jay returned with the arrow. It was a masterpiece in design and engineering. The arrow appeared to be of perfect weight and balance. Somehow, Jay had crafted the syringe to the shaft so flawlessly that it looked as if it had been manufactured just for that purpose.

"Jay, how in the world did you make this. It's a model of perfection."

"With the right tools, it's easier than skinning a cat." Jay answered.

I examined the syringe a little closer. "The syringe is large enough to carry a tranquilizer that should do the job. How much you think Wool…the steer weighs?"

"He's about eight hundred pounds." Bill said.

"Stop by the office later this afternoon. I'll get the tranquilizer ready for you."

"Thanks a lot, Doc. You best hurry on in the shop. It looks like it filling up right much." And with that Arnold and his cohorts left.

I peeped in the door. All the seats were taken and both barber chairs were occupied. "What are the chances, Ricky?"

"Best come back tomorrow, Doc. Otherwise you'd have to wait thirty minutes or more."

Even with loss of time dealing with Arnold about his steer, there was still time to catch lunch. If I hurried I could grab a sandwich and go to the forest for a nice quiet lunch. The temperature was in the seventies. That would be perfect and a nice break in the day. Just as the door closed behind me, the harsh sound of the beeper interrupted my thoughts.

I leaned back on the door and opened it slightly. "Ricky, mind if I use your phone?"

"We don't have one."

"You're kidding! How can you function without a phone?"

"This shop's never had a phone since it was first established back in the fifties. Don't need one. People just come in and get their haircut and leave. Simple as that. When I need to make a call, I just go across the street to the Chamber. They got one."

Of course. Ricky was right, I thought as I walked across the street to the Chamber of Commerce. They didn't operate on an appointment basis and really had no requirement for a phone to conduct business. My practice was so anchored around the need for a phone that I thought everyone needed one. The Chamber lady dialed the number and handed me the receiver across the counter. Susan answered the phone in her usual pleasing way. "Dr. Brooks' office. This is Susan. How may I help you?"

"I got your page. What's up?"

"Mr. Powell called about his mule and said you needed to see it right away."

So much for a leisurely lunch. "How do I get there?" Susan gave me succinct directions and told me I would have to cross a decrepit bridge as I entered the property. "Tell him I'll be there in about thirty minutes. Oh, Susan, call an order for me into the Sub Pub for pick-up. I'll eat it on the way to the Powell place."

"The usual?"

"Yes, that will do and it will be ready fast."

I swung by the sandwich shop and picked up the sandwich and then headed toward East Fork. The drive was a leisurely ten-mile trip through a picturesque area of Transylvania County. The trip ended just upstream from a cascading falls on a branch of the East Fork River. The Powell place was on the other side of the river and I didn't like the look of the bridge I was about to cross. It was an old, wooden bridge with no side railings. There was a double thickness of wood on either side of the bridge where the tires would traverse but there was a plank missing right in the middle of the bridge. The other boards were weatherworn and twisted. Just as I got up my nerve and was inching toward the ramp, a head popped through the gap of the missing plank.

It was Mr. Powell. His mouth fell open and his eyes bulged from their sockets when he saw my truck so close to him. He dropped back down between the planks and made his way to the side of the bridge where he crawled up to the level of the road. He rotated his baseball hat back to its intended position and brushed his soiled overalls with both hands as he walked toward my truck.

"Gave me quite a scare."

"Sorry, Mr. Powell. I didn't know you were under the bridge."

"Not you in particular, sonny. It's those damned snakes. Can't never do any repair work on the bridge without running into one of them. This one was of no harm, though…just a water snake…still startled me some, though. 'Course when I jumped from the snake and stuck my head through that missing plank, there you were. Sorta' got me coming and going. " He said as he walked toward my pickup.

"What kind of repair work did you have to do?"

"Nothing much, just had to shore it up a little. The freezes this winter did some damage to the underpinning. It's been sagging some in the middle, but it'll hold now. Go ahead, Doc, you ain't goin' fall in. I'll join you on the other side."

I eased the truck across the bridge and then navigated through and around a rusted out tractor and two old junk cars. Mr. Powell came to the truck and jumped in. "I best ride with you from here so I can show you to the barn. The mule don't look any too good to me. My sons been farming with me for thirty years, but this one's got them stumped."

As we approached the barn, I could see two men standing next to the worst looking mule I had ever seen. Every bone in his body protruded painfully from his dehydrated hide. His head hung slothfully toward the ground and the drool from his mouth was stringy and off black in color. The poor beast was using all the strength it could muster just to stand up. Even his ears had lost their ability to stand. He was a pitiful sight.

It was already painfully clear there would be little I could do for this animal. One of Mr. Powell's sons came to the truck as I grabbed my bag.

"Sure glad you could come by so quick, Doc. Here, let me take that bag for you."

"How long you had him?" I asked.

"Billy and I bought him yesterday."

I was astounded. "You bought this mule?"

"Sure did. Got a good price, too. My brother Billy said to me, he said, 'That's a good price, Trace. We can't pass this one up'. So we gave the man his money and guess what? He gave us free delivery. We figured we'd get you to fix him up and we would still be money ahead."

I was afraid to ask the purchase price. "Hand me the thermometer, Trace. It's in that plastic case just inside the right-hand compartment of the bag."

The temperature was ninety-six point four. No real surprise. This poor mule was on his way out of this world. His entire neck was as hard as a board and the lymph nodes under his jaw were baseball size. His teeth were too worn to accurately age him. The words wouldn't come to me. How do you tell two exuberant men who thought they had negotiated the deal of their lives that euthanasia was the only real option? Just as I was about to pass my verdict, Mr. Powell interjected.

"I told these boys 'bout the only thing they could do was to take that back hoe over there and dig a hole for him. He's about the worst count mule I believe I've ever laid my eyes on."

"Trace…Billy, the mule's got some kind of disease that has affected his whole system. Cancer, some kind of systemic fungus or something. I don't know for sure. But what I do know is that he's not going to make it regardless of any treatment I can give him. He's so sick that he can't maintain a normal temperature and I'm guessing he's more than thirty years old. He needs to be put down. That's the only humane thing to do."

"Can't do that. We got too much money in him. Give him a shot to make him feel better while we ponder our options." Trace said as he looked at Billy with discouragement.

I went to my bag and examined my thoughts about the futility of any type of treatment as I drew up a dose of vitamins and injected the mule in the rump. He was too sick to move or flinch as I pushed the plunger on the syringe. I assembled my equipment and returned to the truck. Mr. Powell said thanks and not to worry about his boys… they'd get over it.

The return trip to the office was not as pleasant as the drive to the Powell's. Veterinarians are always eager to help and to return a sick animal to health, but nothing short of a miracle was going to reverse the course of their mule's destiny. I could still see the defeat on the men's faces. I had to shake off my own disappointment. Tomorrow would be a new day and within it would be new opportunities.

CHAPTER SIX

"There's a man on the phone who insists on talking only to you. He's says it's a sensitive subject. You would think by now men would just say they had a pet they want you to neuter." Susan handed me the phone and then returned to her work pulling files for the day's schedule.

"Hello, this is Doctor Brooks. How can I help you?"

"Doc, you reckon you could castrate a six-hundred-pound hog?" The man's voice was rough and commanding.

"Six-hundred pounds! Why on earth did you let him get so big?"

"He's a breeding hog, Doc."

Of course. What else would it be? Pigs are castrated by the time they weigh twenty pounds unless they are reserved for breeding. I was just so taken by the size that I didn't know exactly how to handle this particular situation.

"You still there, Doc?"

"Yes, I'm here. I didn't catch your name."

"Didn't give it, but this here is Wiley, Chester Wiley."

"That's a mighty big hog, Mr. Wiley. When did you want to do this?"

"Noon today," he said abruptly. "We caught him and that weren't no easy job. So we want it done now while we got him pinned up."

I fumbled around and found the schedule Susan had just completed. The last morning appointment was 11:00 and then nothing until 1:45. "I can be there around 11:30. Where are you located?"

"I'm up in Quebec community, but that ain't where the hog is. It's down on Frozen Creek Road. You know where that is, don't you?"

"Yes, how far off Highway 64?"

"About a five-minute drive."

"Can you be a bit more specific?"

"I tell you what, Doc. I'm going to be there before you anyway, so I'll just hang an orange bandana on the post that leads to the hog pen."

With those directions given, Mr. Wiley hung up. A six-hundred-pound hog! What was I thinking? In school the most we had ever done was a few little piglets under the best of conditions. There weren't that many hogs in our county so I had never had to castrate one. I had done a few piglets for backyard farmers but nothing even close to this. Now, I had talked myself into a situation I wasn't sure I could handle. I could see the headlines, "Veterinarian Gored To Death Making Futile Attempt To Castrate Hog." I didn't want my last act, my legacy, you might say, to be so ignoble. I grabbed my large animal surgery notes and textbooks and did some serious reading. Funny, some of the material was underlined. I remembered now how we had studied something about castrating production hogs. Not thinking I would ever have to do this, I had given it no more attention than to memorize the information for a test. Now I was about to take the test. I hoped it wouldn't be my final exam.

Susan stirred me from my remorseful thoughts. "Why would anyone want to castrate a hog that size? Wouldn't most farmers just kill the hog and cure the meat?"

"No, a breeding hog is not suitable for eating. The meat is too tough and has a real gamely taste to it from all that testosterone circulating in its body. If they castrate him and wait about two months, he'll be a suitable candidate for a barbecue."

"Oh. Mrs. Owen just turned into the parking lot. She's here with her new Pomeranian."

"What a contrast," I mumbled. My thoughts were still on the six-hundred-pound hog that, in my mind's eye, had tusks eight inches long. Through some misguided delusion, I had unwittingly stretched my imagination to the point that my encounter with this hog was to be a contest. I suddenly knew, without a shadow of a doubt, the thoughts that must have gone through a Roman gladiator's mind some two thousand years ago. Somehow it seemed more honorable to face a lion than a hog. The outcome would certainly be the same.

"Did you say something?"

"Oh, it was nothing. Show Mrs. Owen into the exam room."

"Good morning, Mrs. Owen. Where's that fine little dog we're suppose to examine?"

"I'll get him in just a minute. He's in the reception room with my niece, Jolene. I just wanted you to know what I'm doing before I bring him in. You see, my husband and I don't have any children around the house anymore, so we thought we would start raising Pomeranians." She couldn't contain herself any longer and rushed from the exam room to the reception area and retrieved the little pup from her niece.

"Isn't he just about the cutest thing you've ever seen? I mean, look at his fur. They just don't make Pomeranians with long hair like that. We were real fortunate to find him, and we only had to drive an hour and a half to Sylva Township to find the little darling. His former owner said she really didn't want to part with him...how he was so affectionate and all. But, we changed her mind, we did. We told her about our niece's girl Pomeranian and the good papers it had. Then we really laid it on about the empty nest syndrome and all that and she said, 'You're twisting my arm, but you've convinced me that you will give Puff a good home.' I tell you, right here, how excited I was. We didn't waste a moment because we were afraid she might change her mind, and we went straight to the kitchen to sign all the documents."

Mrs. Owen was beside herself. She was no easy pushover for anyone and her life's struggles were reflected in her wire-like physique and leathery skin. She had come up the road of hard knocks and knew her way around. But when it came to little furry things, that was a different story.

She was without mercy in describing the dog. "He's a proud dog, too, and he's only seven months old. Look how he stands. Proud, isn't he? I just can't imagine why that lady would sell him after raising him from a little pup. Even his color is unique. You just don't find..."

I couldn't take it any longer without a little reprieve so I let her accolades drift into the background as I started the examination. Usually, the exam started at the head and in a very systematic way progressed toward the rear. That way I was sure to check everything from the eyes, ears, teeth, lymph nodes, heart and lungs, abdomen, muscles and skeletal system and then back to the urogenital tract. For some reason, I began in just the opposite direction. That was mistake! How was I going to keep my discovery under control throughout the remainder of the physical?

"His feet are even different. My niece has got the cutest little girl dog. That's who we are going to breed this one to. They are from completely different lines, you know. We wouldn't want to have any incest relationship and end up with some pups with things wrong with them."

The exam was almost over and I had to think of a way to break the news to her.

"Well, how does he check out Doctor Brooks? I just can't wait to get this little fellow about his duty. Jolen's dog is due to come into season just about any day."

I put the stethoscope down and looked Mrs. Owen straight in the eyes. This wasn't exactly the way I planned it but the words just spilled from my mouth uncontrollably. "Mrs. Owen, Puff is cryptorchid."

"I'm sure he's that, Doctor. I mean, he's got all the other good features so why shouldn't he have that too?"

"Mrs. Owen, I'm afraid being cryptorchid isn't a good feature, especially for a breeding dog. He has only one testicle."

"Oh, my goodness. Does that mean he can't get any pups?"

"No, he can still sire, but you won't be able to register pups from a dog that has his condition." I couldn't believe it. Her enthusiasm had not waived even the slightest amount. Her eyes were doing some calculating, as she became quiet for a brief moment.

"That's probably the reason we got such a good deal. You know, we paid only four hundred dollars for him. And besides, we only want a few puppies from him and Jolene's dog won't know the difference."

She moved to the edge of the door and peeked around the corner to see if her niece showed any sudden changes in body language to indicate she might have overheard the rather private conversation. All appeared safe. She motioned to me as she leaned over the table. "Doctor, I'm holding you to the strictest client confidentiality…Don't breathe a word of this to Jolene. I don't want her to think Puff is an invalid. Puff doesn't know it, Jolene doesn't know it. It'll be our secret."

"But, Mrs. Owen, you can't sell the pups since this problem is most likely hereditary."

"Does that mean it is in his blood?"

"Well, yes...so to speak."

"No matter, we just want a few good pups," she said as she picked up Puff and left the room. No sooner had she left than she poked her head back through the door, still gleaming, "How did the rest of him look?"

"Fine, but we need to …"

"Good. You told me all I need to know, and for that matter, all Jolene needs to know, too. Remember, Doctor, it's our secret."

After Mrs. Owen left the office with her little indiscretion in her arms, the morning dispatched itself with unusual haste. Eleven o'clock arrived much too quickly, I thought, and without much mercy on the time I needed to gather my wits about the upcoming call. The size of the hog was a serious concern. A beast that size could spell disaster in the blink of an eye. I had been too eager to take the call in the hopes of building a reputation that I could do just about anything a farmer needed for his livestock. Not much I could do about that now. There was time for a quick call home. Linda's voice would be reassuring.

"Hi, honey. How's your morning going?"

"Great! You know that pocketbook I've been promising myself? Well, it went on sale today, so I bought it. It will be a perfect match to the boots I got last month. I'll show it to you when you come home for lunch."

"That's why I called. I'm going on a call to castrate a hog on Frozen Creek and won't get home for lunch. I'll catch a sandwich on the way back." The afterthought, "if I get back," crossed my mind.

"Do you think it will take long?"

"I'm not sure. He's big. Six hundred pounds. I'm a little worried about how I'm going to constrain him."

"Well, I'm sure you will do just fine. You've done this before, haven't you?"

"Not on one this big."

"What's the biggest one you've ever done?"

"About thirty-five pounds."

"Oh...Don't worry. You've got very quick reflexes, you lift weights and you're strong. How much did you say the pig weighed?"

"It's not a pig. It's a hog and he's about four times my size and he's armed."

"Armed with what?"

"Tusks."

"Tusks? What's that?"

"They are teeth about eight inches long that the hog uses to dig holes and do other things with." My imagination was getting away from me.

"Well, you've got anesthesia and a scalpel. Sounds like a fair match to me. Just kidding. Be careful and don't take any chances. Remember, you have a Boy Scout hike with the boys this weekend. Got to go. I'll leave the sandwich in the fridge. Bye."

Not much sympathy there and she had used the term "fair match". The word "contest" had come to my mind. Neither word conjured pleasant thoughts. The drive to the farm would give me some time to frame my plan of attack. Attack? What was I thinking? I needed to cool down and think logically. The farmer said they had captured the hog and had it ready. Shouldn't be much to it. The hog was probably in some stocks that would prevent it from moving much. I would just slip up, give the proper anesthetic and do the surgery quick and simple. Mark Twain had once said that he worried about an awful lot of things in his life and most of them never happened. I would yield to his wisdom and move on.

Frozen Creek Road was a gravel road that rambled through a heavily wooded area and was occasionally punctuated with a meadow and a small farmhouse. None of the farms could be considered farms in the traditional sense. Some would have a few cattle, maybe a hog or two and chickens. In fact, there seemed to be a lot of chickens. There were rooster hutches by the score and the proud occupant could be seen strutting around his four-foot square piece of territory just daring anything to intrude. A small piece of twine around one of the rooster's legs kept him from roaming into trouble. What in the world could they be doing with all these roosters, I thought. Oh, never mind. I've got trouble enough waiting for me.

Just after crossing a small bridge, I saw the orange bandana tied around a post leading off the road. About one hundred and fifty feet up the road was a man motioning to me to drive toward him. When I got to him, he jumped in the front seat and said, "Drive around that out-building and down through that clump of mountain laurel." The man was huge… about six foot four and at least three hundred pounds. The fact that he hadn't even said hello or any other casual greeting when I arrived had shrunk into insignificance. His knees were crammed into the dashboard of my small truck and his legs were pressing against the floor gearshift lever.

"Excuse me, Mr. Wiley, could you move your leg over a bit?"

"What's that?" he said in harsh voice.

"I can't shift the gears. You need to pull your leg over a little".

"Why don't you get yourself a real truck? The bed on this thing probably wouldn't even hold my hog."

"Probably not. Where's the pen?"

"Just past these laurel. There! You can see the pen over there where the other men are."

The pen didn't look like any other pigpen I had ever seen. It was about fourteen feet square and enclosed by a four-foot concrete wall on all sides. The dirt floor was one foot deeper than the outside level. Right in the middle was the largest hog I had ever seen. He had heard the truck approach and was on the alert with his beady little eyes penetrating me. As I had feared, he was armed with an eight-inch tusk on either side of his snout. The animal had panic in his face and there was a profuse amount of saliva drooling from his mouth. As the hog stirred close to where the three men were leaning over the wall, one of them spit his chewing tobacco in the hog's face. They all laughed and looked in my direction. None of the three men budged as I gathered my equipment.

I laid a cloth on a small growth of grass near the pen and knelt down to put the instruments in order. The kneeling position triggered me to say a little prayer and just as I completed that, Mr. Wiley strolled over to me. I hoped he hadn't seen my hands trembling.

"How are you going to do it?"

I looked up at his huge frame. He had a twisted smile on his face and his deep-seated eyes peered over his nose in a depraved manner. His hands were folded behind his back and he was rocking back and forth on his heels. When I had looked in the pen a few minutes earlier, I had noticed a large number of chicken feathers that had collected in the corners. And the sunken floor allowed those outside the pen to have a clear view of any activity within the pen. It was clear. I had seen the same sort of setup when I was stationed overseas and had gone to the Philippines on temporary assignment. It was a cock-fighting pit! The men now gathered around the pit were not there to help but clearly to see a contest. I was as sure of this as I could be, considering my terrified state of mind. All the roosters I had seen along the road on my way to Wiley's place were future contestants. But for now, I was the attraction. Suddenly, I had a clear insight as to how I could do this procedure and simultaneously spare my life.

"Mr. Wiley, that hog over there is all stirred up. He's scared...probably never been penned up before. Once we start this procedure, he's going to scream bloody murder. We won't be able to talk because of the noise, so everyone must know his job, and your job is to catch the hog and put this snare around his snout. Once you have caught him, I'll give him some sedative and castrate him."

41

Wiley's ruddy complexion suddenly turned as pale as a sheet. His once insolent sneer turned to a dropped lower jaw and a mouth opened in shocked disbelief.

"I thought that was your job."

"Now, Mr. Wiley, how can I catch him, hold him and then run around to his backside and castrate him? It's really quite simple. Just take this snare and slip it in his mouth. When I hear him scream, I'll jump in the pen and give him the sedative. Oh, and Mr. Wiley, I'd be careful of those tusks. They are quite large."

Wiley's pride was too large for him to back down. He walked with uncertainty to the pen and eased himself into the pit. The hog snorted and charged. Wiley demonstrated skillful agility as he hurdled over the wall to safety. He got back into the pit. This time the hog just stared and then suddenly lunged. Wiley barely escaped and was over the wall again and back to safety. The hog seemed to dare him to try again. His friends began harassing him and teased his ineptness. I was beginning to become concerned. Surely Wiley had snared a hog before, but his skill was lacking and he was fatiguing quickly. Sweat was pouring off his brow.

"This hog is smart," I shouted. "You men give him a hand."

Instantly, the mood changed. The teasing that was flowing so freely from their mouths ceased. By this time, they too could see the time for getting serious was at hand. Wiley was leaning against a tree trying to catch his breath while one of the men fetched a loose fence gate and brought it to the pen. One man distracted the hog while the other two cornered it with the gate. Panic overtook the hog as he fought to free himself. The hog's thrashing was powerful. His tusks caught under the gate and, with a mighty upward thrust, threw one of the men against the wall. The man charged back to his position. The men struggled to press the hog against the wall. "Get that snare over here," one yelled in a panic. By that time Wiley had caught his wind and was able to put the snare over the hog's snout.

Once the snare was in place, the six-hundred-pound hog was neutralized. I jumped in the pit and inserted the hypodermic needle with the anesthesia into his ear vein. The hog slowly dropped. I quickly cleaned the scrotal area, made the incision and castrated the beast. All the men had collapsed from their ordeal and missed the show they came to see.

"Good job, Mr. Wiley. I know who I can count on if I ever need any help on anyone else's hog."

"Well... that wouldn't be me. I only do that for my own hogs, and I don't have any after this one." Wiley's color had returned to his face but the sneer was absent. He paid me and I left. As I drove past the roosters on my way out, I could only think about what was waiting for them. Somehow, I wished I could tell them that today the underdog was the victor.

CHAPTER SEVEN

When I opened my office in Brevard, my plan was to practice both small and large animal veterinary medicine. There simply wasn't enough large animal work to support a practice and there was already a small animal clinic in the city. I knew I would have to derive a living by working with both farm animals and domestic pets. What I didn't really understand were the complexities of juggling the two entities. The task was enormous. First, there were the equipment and supplies for the small animal side of the practice: surgical equipment, an x-ray machine, vaccines, dental instruments, laboratory equipment, pharmaceuticals, exam tables, instrument sterilizers, and countless other pieces of equipment. Second, I would have to do essentially the same thing to support the large animal side. Unfortunately, there was little of this type of equipment that could serve dual purposes in both areas. Both small animal work and large animal work had their own special needs.

For the first several years, the balancing act went well. Susan and I divided the office duties so that we covered all the important areas. Few things fell between the cracks. Because of Susan's excellent administrative ability, I was freed from many of the business aspects of the practice. Susan took care of the inventory control, account management, and the myriad of other management areas that make a business run smoothly. But the practice was moving more and more into small animal. When I was on a farm call, Susan usually spent her time managing the various aspects of the office. With a shift toward small animals, the office itself became busier. That meant Susan had less time to manage. Her time was consumed with telephone duties, scheduling, talking to clients in the office, assisting me in surgery, and in general being a good receptionist. Just before both of us went crazy, we came to the same conclusion: it's time to hire a veterinary technician. That would free both of us to pursue our primary area of focus. It took us about a month to find the perfect person and her name was Alma.

Alma handed me the medical chart for "Beau," a seven-year-old Labrador retriever owned by Bob Palmer. She had noted in the record that Beau had a large swollen area under his right eye.

"Show Mr. Palmer in the exam room, Alma. I'll be right there." Bob Palmer was one of my heroes. Over the past several years, I had gotten to know him and had learned a little about his background. He never volunteered much information, but he was the age that would have put him into the World War II generation. On one visit I asked him, "Bob, did you serve during World War Two?"

"Yep, sure did. Went in as a boy of eighteen in 'forty-one' and came out a man in 'forty-five.'"

"What branch were you in?"

"Navy."

"What was your specialty?"

"Mostly revolved around aircraft. My last assignment was as a Chief Petty Officer of the Martin PBM Mariner. That was a twin engine amphibious aircraft equipped for antisubmarine warfare. It had a crew of seven most of the time. On special missions, we would add an eighth crew member."

"I didn't realize we had antisubmarine aircraft in World War Two."

"That Mariner was quite a bird. It could carry up to eight thousand pounds of depth charges and had eight fifty-caliber machine guns for defense. We were all crossed trained as gunners. So when things got hot I would man one of the guns."

"Wow, that must have been exciting." I couldn't contain myself. There in front of me was a man of medium statue, about five-foot nine and of a very unassuming nature. He was probably one of the most gentle men I had ever met. He always wore a big smile and a crazy little hat that cradled itself just a bit from his forehead. On that aircraft his job would have been to defend the aircraft from hostile attack as it dived on a submarine.

"Exciting is not exactly the way I saw it. It was more like stark raving terror about two hours every day."

"Of course. Exciting isn't the right word. What you and your generation did was extraordinary. You're one of my heroes." I meant this sincerely. Men such as Bob were literally jerked from their youth and thrown into the horrors of war. "I can't imagine what it was like to dive at two-hundred fifty miles per hour on a sub and to be firing a machine gun at the same time."

"The fear was before and after the flight when there was time to think about it. We were too busy during the fight to be scared."

I remember we talked some more. Bob never bragged about his experience. Once he even lamented about the poor German sailors that were blasted from the waters.

"They really had no chance after the code was busted. We intercepted their orders and knew where they were going to be before they ever got there. We hit them hard...really hard. They were soldiers like us. Terrible thing...war."

There was little I could say. He had been there. I had not. He was becoming melancholy and the smile was fading from his face. I changed the subject and never mentioned it again.

Today he brought Beau to see me because there was a swelling under the right eye. Beau weighed about ninety pounds so it took the two of us to hoist him onto the exam table. I opened Beau's mouth and quickly saw a fracture at the gum line of the upper fourth premolar tooth. The tooth had become infected and had formed a pus pocket at its roots located just under the eye. "I see the problem, Bob. This tooth is fractured and has festered under the eye."

"You know, Doc, about two weeks ago the darnedest thing happened. If I hadn't seen it myself, I wouldn't think it possible. Beau missed a step next to our retaining wall and fell about five feet. He had a little blood from his mouth but I couldn't find the source. He recovered real quick from the fall so I didn't pay much more attention to it. I bet that's when he broke that tooth."

"Leave Beau with me this morning and I'll take that tooth out and drain the abscess. He'll be fine."

Bob gave Beau a hug and left. Alma patted Beau on the head as she grasped his left front leg so the vein would show up. I gave him a small dose of anesthetic and extracted the tooth. The upper fourth premolar tooth has three roots anchoring it to the skull and is normally difficult to extract. The tooth came out easily, almost too easily. There was a small sore next to the tooth on the hard palate which had probably been caused by the fall from the retaining wall. I rubbed Beau on the head as he was regaining consciousness. "That must have been quite a fall, old boy, but you labs are a tough breed and don't complain much."

I placed Beau on a blanket in the kennel and dialed Bob's number. "The tooth came out just fine, Bob, but I think we need to watch Beau closely over the next week or so. I'm putting him on antibiotics. I'm concerned there might be more to this abscess than just a broken tooth."

"Like what?"

46

"It's probably nothing. The tooth seemed to come out a lot easier than expected. Let's just watch Beau for a few days and if the swelling recurs, bring him right back so we can recheck him."

"Okay, Doc. I'll pick him up around five."

No sooner had I said goodbye than I heard a confusion of hysterical cries in the waiting room. Alma darted into my office. "The Snyders just ran over their dog and are in a terrible way. I'm more worried about Mr. Snyder than his dog. Sweat is pouring down his face and he's white as a sheet. Mrs. Snyder is trying to comfort him but is not having much luck. I'll show them in the exam room and get everything ready. See what you can do to calm him down a bit. He really has me concerned."

Alma hadn't exaggerated. When I saw Mr. Snyder, he was bent over the dog and sobbing uncontrollably. His wife was behind him and was rubbing his shoulders in a futile attempt to ease his grief. The Snyders were summertime visitors to Brevard and we saw them a couple times each season. Mr. Snyder was in his seventies and not in the best of health. He had had bypass surgery three years ago. His face was an ashen gray. The world revolved around his little Chinese Pug, Snuggles. He had told me more than once that he would die if anything ever happened to his dog. Seeing him now in such a distraught condition punctuated that statement.

"Mr. Snyder, let me take a look at Snuggles."

"Have mercy on me. I can't believe I ran over my own dog. I was just backing the car to connect the trailer, and then I felt a bump and then heard that terrible scream. Then there was more screaming. I felt like my heart had been ripped from my chest." He relinquished his smothering clutch on Snuggles, turned to his wife and wrapped his arms around her in desperation. His legs were unsteady.

I quickly examined Snuggles and determined she had a pelvic fracture. A survey of her vital signs was encouraging. By this time, Mrs. Snyder had managed to move her husband to a chair and was attending to him by wiping his brow with her handkerchief.

"She's going to die, isn't she? And I will have killed her."

"She has some serious injuries, but none of them seem life-threatening. She has a fractured pelvis and..."

"A fractured what?"

"Her hip is broken, Mr. Snyder. We're going to get started on her right away and will do everything we can. I want you to go back to the campground and get some rest. There's no need for you to sit here and worry. You'll do better in your own surroundings."

47

"Can't do that, Doc. I'll just sit out there in your waiting room."

I picked up Snuggles and carried her back to the surgery. Alma, in her usual efficient way, had readied everything we needed to start an IV. Once we had the fluids flowing, we moved Snuggles to the x-ray room to take pictures of the chest and abdominal areas. We were taking measurements when Susan rushed into the room. "Mr. Snyder almost collapsed so his wife rushed him to the hospital."

"Why didn't she call EMS?"

"She said she recognized the signs and that she could get him down there faster than they could. Just before they left, Mr. Snyder reached in his pocket and pulled out a medicine vial and put a pill under his tongue."

Alma and I looked at each other and simultaneously said: "Nitroglycerin!"

"You think so?" Susan said.

"Probably. He does have a heart condition." I said as we rushed to finish the measurements.

The radiographs confirmed a syphyseal fracture of the pelvis – the area where the left and right halves of the pelvis join on the underside of the belly. There was also a separation of the right sacroiliac junction. This junction connects the pelvis to the spine. Pelvic fracture repair can be a complicated and sophisticated affair and is usually handled by a specialist. If the fractures don't involve the hip joint, they will often heal without surgery. This fracture, unfortunately, was unstable. Without at least some minimal form of repair, the dog would not be able to stand and would be in terrible pain. The midline of the pelvis had separated and Snuggles was unable to pull her legs underneath her. The sacroiliac luxation complicated things. On top of all this, Snuggles was twelve years old and wouldn't do well with a long surgery. I prepared to repair the syphyseal fracture to stabilize the pelvis. Such a repair was within my capability. I didn't have either the equipment or the expertise to repair the sacroiliac luxation. But I knew it would heal on its own to a satisfactory degree.

Snuggles had another concern. She was a Chinese Pug. These flat-faced dogs have several respiratory compromises. In short, they are a serious anesthetic risk. All her vital signs were good so we decided to proceed with the surgery. Alma was monitoring the anesthesia and I had just made the approach incision when Susan called on the intercom.

"The physician assistant at the emergency room just called. He said if that dog dies, you might as well dig two holes. He's got Mr. Snyder on oxygen and some sort of IV drip to sedate him a bit."

"Great! Nothing like a little pressure to complicate things." In another ten minutes, I had dissected the muscles beneath the pelvic symphysis and exposed the fracture. I drilled four stabilizing holes and pulled the fracture together with stainless steel wire. Snuggles had been under anesthesia for forty-five minutes. "How's the patient doing?"

"She's doing great." Alma answered. "Should I reduce the anesthesia a bit?"

"Yea. I'm almost ready to close the muscle layer. Then it won't take any time to close the skin."

In another fifteen minutes, I finished the closure. Snuggles began to stir a little and gagged as Alma eased the anesthetic tube from the windpipe. She recovered well and was sitting up about thirty minutes later.

"Okay, Susan, now we can call the emergency room and give Mr. Snyder the good news. Who knows we might have saved two patients today and it's only twelve thirty."

Susan smiled and reminded me that appointments were going to start at one-fifteen.

Brevard is a small town and there is a local joke that you can get anywhere you need to be within five minutes. So it was with lunch. Rocky's with its fifties-styled soda fountain would be perfect. I would just dart in there and have a quick sandwich and a coke.

Why do things never go as planned? Dwayne was sitting at the counter and the only available stool was next to him. Now, I don't have anything against Dwayne. He's just different. He talks incessantly...about everything...and nothing. When he is finished talking, the listener is exhausted.

I didn't want to appear rude and neither did I want to engage Dwayne in conversation so I just slipped on the stool next to him and said, "Hello, Dwayne. I hope Bob is serving fast today because I'm running out of time. By the way, do you know what time it is?"

"Funny you should say that."

"Say what, Dwayne?"

"That you are running out of time."

"Why's that?"

"I mean, how can you run out of time? You see, I've been contemplating time lately and have decided it is a peculiar thing."

"Peculiar? In what way?" That was a question I should have

49

left undiscovered.

"You asked the time, right?"

"Yes, but it seems like there would be a simple answer."

"There's not," Dwayne responded. "You see, you didn't state if you wanted Eastern Standard Time, Mountain Time, Central Standard Time or Pacific Coast Time."

"Dwayne, we are sitting at a lunch stool in western North Carolina, so that's the time I want."

"You've got relatives in California, don't you?"

"Yes, but..."

"How could it be that we are eating lunch and they are just finishing breakfast? You see, we have only covered a few of the different kinds of time out there. And then, of course, there are all sorts of associated times?"

"Associated times! What are you referring to now?" Again the words left my mouth before I considered the consequences.

"Associated times would include all sorts of things. There would be school time, work time, time off, double time, time and a half, Greenwich meantime, lunch time anytime, some time, good time, bad time, lapsed time, lost time, timeless, timely, vacation time, present time..."

Mercifully, Bob came to take my order.

"The usual, Doc?"

"The usual, oh and Bob, could you hurry please? I'm running late."

Incredibly, Dwayne was still at it. "...past time, future time, daylight savings time, overtime, spare time..."

"Great, Dwayne, you've made your point."

"But the one that really gets me is wasted time. What happens to wasted time? I mean, like, where does it go? Dwayne was staring at the wall with a glazed look on his face, and there was a pause, but not for long. "Then there's killing time. Does that mean I'm endangering eternity if I kill time. I tell you the truth, Doc, time is a confusing thing."

Bob placed my tuna fish sandwich on the counter. "Bob, could you put that in a bag, please. I'll have to eat this on the run or I'll miss my appointment time."

"See? There's another one: appointment time. There are too many times to keep up with. I think I'll just give up this time thing all together. Thanks, Doc, for helping me work through this." Dwayne swirled around and slid off his stool.

"Dwayne, before you leave, could you tell me what time it is here...in Brevard?"

"Sorry, the battery in my watch rolled over and died on me yesterday." And with that, Dwayne left.

"It's one o'clock," Bob said. "If it's any consolation, you're the third one who endured 'time' with Dwayne at lunch today. The others...they just got up and left...one before I could even fill his order. Oh, you better get that right ear of yours checked out."

"Why's that?"

"It's a mite bit red, like it has a callus on it or something from all that listening."

"Right, Bob. See you next time."

What an experience! Dwayne wanted to know where wasted time went. After this ordeal, I believe I had the answer. I finished the sandwich on my way back to the office where my one-fifteen appointment was waiting. Billy Powell and his brother, Trace, came into the exam room with their dog, Blue.

"Doc, appears we ain't having much luck with our animals lately. Blue doesn't look a heap better than that mule of ours that died in April." Billy put the Treeing Walker hound dog on the exam table.

"Sorry to hear about your mule. Let's see if we can figure out what is going on with Blue." Some people have things so hard that when a bad thing happens, it just seems to soak into a background of misery. I thought this was the case with the Powell brothers. The dog they brought to me to examine was in miserable condition. It was a young dog...three years old by the owner's record. He was infested with ticks and fleas and an intestinal parasite check revealed hookworms and whipworms. By some trick of fate, he had been spared heartworms. At thirty-two pounds, he was at least twenty pounds underweight. But that wasn't what concerned me the most. His lymph nodes were huge and protruding on his skeletal-looking frame. There are many things that can cause enlarged lymph nodes such as cancer, infections, systemic fungal diseases and some others.

I pointed to one of the lymph nodes in front of Blue's left shoulder. "I would like to take an aspiration of this lymph node. It might help me come to a diagnosis."

"What's an aspiration and while you're at it, what's a lymph node?"

"A lymph node is sort of a filtering system in the body. Of course, it has other purposes, too, but sometimes we can stick a needle in one of them and get some idea of what's going on inside the body."

"If that will help, go ahead." Trace said.

Alma brought in the aspiration needle and slides. We collected about four good samples from the prescapular lymph node in front of the left shoulder and two samples from the mandibular lymph node under the jaw. The process to stain and dry the slides took about fifteen minutes. One look under the microscope and we had the answer.

I went back into the exam room. "Billy, what did you do with the mule that died?"

"Buried him."

"How deep?"

"Well, the back hoe weren't working so we had to dig by hand. Not too deep, I reckon. Probably only two feet of dirt on top of the mule."

"Did you put lime in the hole to help with decomposition?"

"No, we just drug him about three feet from where he dropped."

"The mule had some of the same symptoms that Blue has and I'm trying to put the two things together, but I really don't see how the mule could have given this condition to the dog."

"What if Blue had eaten some of the mule?" Billy blurted out.

"But you buried him!"

"That we did, but Blue dug into the grave and, well...it's none too pleasant, but he was rolling in the hole and eating on part of that carcass when we caught him."

Trace trumped in: "Terrible sight, but we got him off as soon as we caught him. He probably hadn't been there more than thirty minutes. But, Doc, that was back in April and here we are in August."

"The slides we made from Blue's lymph nodes were loaded with a fungus called Blastomyces. It's definitely what is causing Blue his problem and I'm guessing the mule was the source."

"Well, I'll be. Who'd ever think a dog could catch a disease from a mule." Billy said as he sat down on the chair next to the exam table.

"He didn't exactly catch the disease from the mule. The fungus was seeded in the mule and he just got exposed to it. It's like rubbing dirt into a wound. Bacteria, or in this case, a fungus entered into his system and infected the dog. It can take anywhere from six weeks to several months for the disease to show up."

"What about Blue? Anything we can do for him?"

"There's a treatment for him, but first we've got to get him in better shape from his other problems. Let's treat the parasite problems first and get some weight on him. The treatment for Blastomycosis is hard on a dog, and Blue needs to be in better shape before we start with that."

The Powell brothers left with medications and promised to return in three weeks for another evaluation of their dog. We never saw Blue again. About a month later I bumped into Mr. Powell and he related the fate of Blue. The brothers were so concerned about the possibility of their other animals getting the same disease that they dug up the mule that very day and poured two hundred pounds of lime in the hole and then covered it back up. They forgot to fence off the area. Blue went back in the hole and, in his digging, covered himself with lime. The boys heard him howling and when they found him, his skin looked like it was on fire. He was rubbing his face ferociously in the ground in an attempt to rid the lime from his eyes. Trace told his father he couldn't stand looking at his dog that way. So he went back to the house, got his rifle and put Blue out of his misery. Mr. Powell said he thought he had taught his boys better judgment on how to pick animals, but he could see, as he put it, "They need more learning."

CHAPTER EIGHT

The phone's ring jerked me into consciousness. As I rolled over to lift the receiver, I saw the clock. It was 6:30 a.m.

"Hello…Who?" I rubbed my eyes and fought back a yawn as I swung my legs over the edge of the bed. "Whose farm?…What seems to be the problem?…Yes, that could be. How long have you been watching her?…Okay, sure. I'll be there in about forty-five minutes."

"Who was that so early on a Saturday morning?" Linda asked.

"That was a man by the name of Bob Wilson. He and another man agreed to watch Orville McKinney's farm while he's away a few days. They came from Atlanta looking for a restful weekend on a mountain farm. It seems Mr. McKinney didn't tell them he had two cows in a delicate condition."

"Why in the world would he be scheduling cows to calve in the late summer?"

"I've been to that farm before. Mr. McKinney doesn't have his heifers separated well from the bull. The heifers probably went into heat and the bull was there to oblige both their hormonal urges. In any event, the two men were out early this morning attending to a newborn calf. What concerns them is that they also found another heifer in distress. She is running through the lot with two feet protruding from her vulva."

"Oh, that's awful. You need to get out there right away. Do you want me to fix some breakfast?"

"No time. I'm going to run right out there. I'll be back in time for the hike. The boys and I packed all our equipment last night."

"Okay, honey. Be careful. Sounds like it might be dangerous."

The McKinney farm was in the Little River district of the county. This was one of my favorite areas. The farms and meadows were cradled between two mountain groups. At certain spots, the scenery was breath taking, and I hadn't been out here at this time in the morning for several months. The fog rising off the French Broad River was floating down the meadows and casting a picture book presentation to an already gorgeous place. I turned in the drive and up the hill leading to the barn. There I could see two men in a frenzy chasing a cow into a small, fenced-in lot. The cow charged one of the men who vaulted over the fence with the expertise of a rodeo cowboy.

"I'm going to feel that tomorrow." He said as he approached me. "My name's Bob Wilson and this other city slicker over here is Randy Arnold." He wiped his hands on what appeared to be fresh bought blue jeans and extended his hand. "We surely appreciate your coming out at this hour on Saturday morning to help us out."

Randy dusted off his shirt and moved toward the two of us. "You'd think that cow would settle down. Man, she's a pistol! It hasn't exactly been the restful weekend we had in mind, but we surely can't say it's been boring either. Bob and I came up from Atlanta to relieve Orville for the weekend. Orville's been talking up this farming thing to us ever since he moved here five years ago. We thought we'd give it a look and see if we might want to find us a little vacation cottage for our two families."

"We haven't set foot off this place since we arrived Thursday night." Bob interjected. "First one cow pushed through a weakness in the fence. We managed to get her back without too much trouble, but it took us another two hours to repair the damage. Then there was that horrible...I guess you would call it bellowing...during the night from the cow that was calving. Neither of us got any sleep. Of course, we didn't recognize what was going on until we found the calf yesterday morning. Then it took us most of the day to do the chores since we didn't know exactly what we were doing or where anything was."

"We were so worn out last night," Randy said, "that we collapsed on that fine porch of Orville's, propped our feet on the railing and drank a beer. We thought we had been initiated and that the worst was behind us. Then this morning the bellowing started again but had an agonizing sound to it. When we saw those two feet protruding from the cow's behind, we knew we were in trouble. Orville had left your name and number stuck to the refrigerator, so we called you right away."

We walked to the lot where the two men had confined the cow. She had settled down a little but had a distressed look in her eyes. As we eased over the fence and walked closer to her, I detected a foul odor. The heifer stared at us as we worked our way toward her rear.

"I thought so. She has an infection. Do you smell that horrible odor?"

"Yeah, I'm afraid to ask what it is," said Bob.

"This heifer's been attempting to have this calf for at least two days. She's probably no more than twenty-two months old and, to put it simply, her pelvis is too small to deliver the calf. The calf got trapped inside and died. Now it is in the stage of decomposition."

"That sounds awful. What's going to happen now?"

"Let's go back to the truck and get organized. This isn't going to be too pleasant."

As we gathered around the truck, I gave the men a little more detail because I wanted to see if they would be able to help me. They had never seen a cow give birth much less had to assist in a delivery. In this case, we had a beef cow that had never been handled other than to be crowded into a cattle chute where she had been vaccinated and wormed. She was wild and scared, a dangerous combination. To make matters worse, she was sick and wouldn't stand up well under stress. By their own definition, these men were city slickers who weren't used to the ways of cattle. I would need their help but not at the risk of their getting injured.

"This is going to be a nasty affair. The calf has putrefied and is too large to come out without some strong pulling. I'm going to give the heifer a slight sedative and then attach a calf jack to the calf's feet and pull the fetus out."

"What's a calf jack?" Bob asked.

"It's this device right here. That curved piece of metal fits under the vulva and behind the cow's hips. Then that four-foot rod inserts into the slot in it. The 'come-along' apparatus that hooks on the rod is connected to the calf's feet and then the calf is 'jacked' from the cow."

"Ouch!" said Randy.

"It's not as bad as it seems. We won't pull that hard. It just allows us to gain a little leverage on the calf that's in there. If we find we're getting too much resistance, we'll stop and go to plan B."

"What's plan B?"

"You don't want to know unless we have to do it. Now, when we go back in there, the first thing I have to do is give a sedative. I'll be giving it in the rear leg and I want ya'll to stand clear when I do that. She's liable to kick or do some other crazy thing. Safety is key here. Do ya'll think you're up to this?"

Both men demonstrated that certain level of confidence I wanted to see. Randy climbed over the fence and Bob passed the jack through the slats to him. The cow was up and sensing we were about to do something. I motioned for the men to stay back as I eased toward the cow. With a quick move I injected the sedative in her rear leg and jumped to the side of her. As I did, she kicked violently with her right rear leg just barely missing me. There was a loud crack as her leg went into full extension. The two men did not have a clear view of things from their angle and were concerned as I made my way back toward them.

"Are you okay? We heard that bone cracking sound and thought she must have broken your leg."

"I'm fine. That sound…" I was just about to explain that the sound they had heard was a normal sound when a cow kicks its rear leg so as to fully extend the leg. It's like our joints that occasionally crack when we move but when that same thing happens in an eight hundred pound heifer, the sound is magnified ten times. The explanation was interrupted as the cow charged us. We jumped on the railing of the fence and then over the top to avoid the heifer's temper tantrum. From that vantage point we saw the effect of the sedative as it gently spread throughout the cow's body.

"Okay, let's get to work." I said as we crossed over the fence and attached the jack to the rear quarters of the heifer that was now lying on the ground. Once the parts were assembled, I put on two shoulder length gloves and began the extraction effort. I asked Bob to work the jack as I slipped my hands into the vaginal area to manipulate the calf. Randy assisted Bob as I positioned the calf's legs to prevent harm to the cow. All of us were on the ground in awkward positions in order to do the work. Bob and Randy were kneeling, one behind the other, with their arms bracing the rod while they worked the jack. I was straddled immediately behind the cow with my gloved hands first on the calf's legs and then inside the vaginal area of the cow. The odor was awful. It's difficult to describe how bad, but let me try. It's your worst biology experiment – gone bad. It's like returning from a two-week vacation to find a piece of spoiled chicken in the refrigerator that is stewing in its own juice. If the odor by itself didn't turn your stomach, add the visual image of thick pus draining from the cow's vaginal area on a hot morning and you'll have the picture. It's enough to make a man sick. And that is exactly what happened. I looked behind me to find only Randy working the jack and he wasn't looking too good.

"Where's Bob?"

"He'll be back in a minute." Randy said as he half-heartily worked the jack.

I continued to manipulate the calf as we were making slow but steady progress. "Lift the rod a little higher, Randy, so I can get a better angle."

"Randy's not back here. He had to leave."

I looked over to my right and there was Randy hunched over and vomiting so bad he actually went down on his knees. He gagged a few more times and then wobbled back to his position on the jack.

"You fellows going to be okay?"

"We'll be fine, Doc. That's some awful smell. How can you stand it?"

"I guess I'm just used to it."

The delivery was near completion. I disconnected the jack and manipulated the calf's body a little to the left and it slipped from the cow to the ground. The ordeal was over.

"You fellows did an outstanding job," I said in hopes of encouraging two men whose colorless, pasty faces told the story of where they wished they hadn't spent this weekend. They staggered to their feet and, with great effort, picked up the jack and climbed over the fence. As they made their way to the truck, I flushed the cow's uterus twice with an antiseptic solution and then put two large antibiotic tablets deep into the uterus.

I made my way across the lot and climbed over the fence. At the top of the fence, I paused a moment to observe both men sitting on the tail gate of the truck with their heads staring aimlessly toward the ground. Exhaustion and nausea were their companions at the moment. "Real troopers," I thought. These men had the tenacity to stick to a really horrible job…part from their responsibility to their friend whose farm they had agreed to watch for the weekend and part from my need for their assistance. They may have been city slickers, but they had done this job as well as many seasoned farmers I had seen over the years.

"Well, Bob, Randy, it was good meeting you. This experience has been a rude initiation into the life of a cattle farmer, but, I must say, y'all did superb." Both men had anemic but satisfied smiles on their faces as I explained to them how to dispose of the dead calf and how to care for the cow over the next twenty-four hours.

"We'll come by Monday on our way to Atlanta to pay the bill if that's all right with you."

"Sure, that's fine. Now, you two need to have some fun this weekend. You should get cleaned up and go to the forest, visit Looking Glass Falls and just kick back. You did more work before lunch today than most men do in an entire day." With that I left. Their exhausted, feeble wave good-bye told the story. The forest wouldn't see them today, but I imagined the porch, the rocker chair and a beer would.

By the time I arrived home, Keith and Wyatt were putting the final touches to their overnight packs. Linda was giving last minute instructions on how to handle blisters and how to recognize poison ivy.

"Mom...we know all that stuff. You know they teach us that at scouts," Keith said.

I took a quick shower and loaded our equipment and the boys into the car. When we arrived at the scout hut, Bill Huters, the scoutmaster, was checking every scout to insure each boy had what he needed and didn't have what he didn't need. He had rigged up a scale, similar to those in a grocery store, that hung from a limb of the tree to insure each boy's backpack was within that individual's limit.

Ray Dunkelberg, a physician friend of mine, and I were the two assistant scoutmasters who would assist Bill with the twelve scouts. We also had one Eagle Scout with us. We loaded the equipment into the van and then drove about twenty-five miles to the Looking Glass trailhead just off the Blue Ridge Parkway. The view was breath taking. Almost every step of the hike we were about to take had its own spectacular vista of the Blue Ridge Mountain range. The hike was just an overnight trip so we didn't have a lot of extra supplies to take, but we did have a fifteen-pound ham and all the fixings that had to be toted to the campsite. Bill distributed that food between the scoutmasters and then gave one last admonition to the boys before we started: "Boys, you all know Dr. Ray. He's here to help any of you who get sick or injured. And, you know Dr. Clyde. He's here for any of you who act like jackasses." We had a great hike. No one got sick or injured and no one required my services either.

On Monday morning I drove to a Holstein cattle farm in Rosman, about ten miles south of Brevard, to test the cows for brucellosis and tuberculosis. Cattle must have these tests for public health reasons. Processing cattle like this can be enjoyable outdoor work for a veterinarian when everything is organized well, and the farm managers had done a good job in preparing for today's work. Brucellosis testing requires a blood sample of each animal and the state has a very precise manner as to how the blood collection vials are to be handled and packed for shipment to the state diagnostic lab. The men knew how to mark and keep all the blood vials in order so this wouldn't be a problem. To test a cow for TB, I would have to inject each cow with a very small amount of tuberculin in the side of the tail just as it joins the body. Three days later we would have to check these injection sites to see if any reactions were present. The trick was how to collect the blood samples, normally gathered from the neck, and do the injections in the tail without a lot of wasted time. Cows can get stressed and overheated if confined in a chute or close quarters too long. We wanted to finish the work before ten o'clock since the temperature and humidity would be creeping up by then.

The cows were channeled through a narrow set of gates that gradually became no wider than the cow itself. At this point the cow would enter into the main chute, which had a head gate that would hold the animal while I did the work. There was an overhead crossbeam connecting the last set of railings leading to the head gate. This is where I could save some time. I could sit on this cross beam and work above the cows. The cows would come through the gate beneath me and would be caught by the farm hand in the head gate. Then all I had to do was gather the blood sample from the tail vein that ran on the underside of the tail instead of gathering the sample from the neck. From this position I could also inject the tail for the TB test. The work went well and after about an hour, we had processed the sixty-five cows. I packaged the samples and drove back to the office and reported for the morning appointments.

"I understand you had a very interesting weekend." Susan said.

"The hike was great."

"I'm not talking about that. I was referring to the calf delivery at the McKinney farm."

"I've had better beginnings to a Saturday morning."

"They were in this morning to pay for the farm call. You've got two admirers in those two men."

"What do you mean by that statement?"

"You could do no wrong according to them."

"They just don't know me very well, that's all."

"According to them you not only earned your pay that day, but you also performed a miracle."

"A miracle? How's that?"

"Yes, a miracle. They said when you sedated the cow…let me put it in their exact words… 'the cow kicked him and broke his leg. Even though Doc tried to down play what happened, we knew his leg was broken because we could hear the bone crack twenty feet away.' Then they talked about the horrible odor but how you just stayed there to deliver the calf and to save the cow. And then how dedicated you were to your boys."

"I mentioned to them I was taking them on a hike. What's so unusual about that?"

"It was beyond them how you could possibly manage with a broken leg. They said you were an encouragement to both of them and that they were going home with a whole new outlook."

"Hey, that's great. I guess I never got around to explaining what that bone cracking sound really was. It's good to feel like a hero ever once in a while."

"That's okay. I told them."

"Told them what?"

"About the bone cracking sound. I told them that when a cow kicked its leg into full extension, a crack could be heard," Susan said.

"Gee, thanks Susan. I guess I didn't even get my fifteen minutes of fame."

"Just kidding," she said as a grin came across her mouth. "Why would I want to mess up such admiration? Your secret is safe with me."

CHAPTER NINE

Over the years I have seen how people can tolerate just about anything to a point and then, when the effort becomes too great, explode with drastic and inappropriate action. Desperation can be disproportionate, and it can be ugly. Such is the case with Mr. Samuel Littleton and his Siamese cat, Trouble, appropriately named I might add. Trouble had a urinary problem known as feline urologic syndrome, or FUS for short. A male cat with this problem is in serious condition and will die if not treated immediately. A brief anatomy lesson is in order here. Urine exits the bladder to the outside of the body through a tube known as the urethra. In the male cat the diameter of this tube becomes progressively smaller throughout its short path from the bladder to the tip of the penis. The slightest thing, a small mineral stone or even a mucous plug, can block the flow of urine and spell disaster. Trouble was the recipient of this malady.

About a year ago in October, Mr. Littleton had rushed into my office with a look of sheer horror on his face. "Trouble can't urin…uh urin…he can't pee! He keeps going to his box trying but nothing's happening." He placed Trouble on the exam table and unwrapped the towel he had placed around him. Mr. Littleton's hands were swollen and deformed from arthritis so the normally simple process of undraping a towel was painfully arduous.

Trouble was typical of a cat with FUS. He was dehydrated, depressed and despondent. I felt in the rear portion of his abdomen and located the hard, baseball size urinary bladder. I explained to Mr. Littleton that I needed to drain the bladder and install a urinary catheter to relieve the crisis. We would keep Trouble a few days, rehydrate him and make sure he could urinate before we sent him home. Mr. Littleton was content with that approach and left his cat for us to begin treatment.

Trouble did well for about five months and then had a recurrence. Mr. Littleton was quick to spot the problem this time and brought Trouble for treatment before dehydration had occurred. He was proud he had recognized and caught the problem so quickly and said, "Put another catheter in him, Doc, and fix him up like you did last time and I'll pick him up on Thursday." It seemed that simple to the owner, but in reality it was much more serious. Trouble had a very small urethra and another catheterization would probably create some scar tissue that would make a recurrence even more likely. I explained a surgical alternative to him that I had done dozens of times on cats that had recurrent urinary blockages.

"You're going to do what? Let me get this straight. You want to, as I see it, amputate his private part, change his plumbing and make him look like a female cat!"

"That's putting it a tad bit more bluntly than I would have. You see, the urethra in a male cat is narrow at the very tip but about three-quarters of an inch further up the opening is much larger. We can access that larger diameter through a surgical procedure. Unfortunately, it does mean he will look like a female cat in that tiny, little area when it's all finished, but really, Mr. Littleton, I don't believe anyone will notice."

Mr. Littleton was a man of few words. "What's the down side?"

"Scar tissue. Since we are operating on a very small structural opening, the healing process could produce scar tissue that will cause another blockage. However, I know Trouble already has scar tissue and will certainly have another episode if we don't take more aggressive measures."

Mr. Littleton agreed and I proceeded with the surgery. Everything seemed to have gone fine over the next seven months, which ended abruptly this morning.

I was just about to give some vaccinations when Susan opened the door to the exam room. "Dr. Brooks, may I see you a moment?" Susan wouldn't do that without good reason so I excused myself from my client and left the exam room.

"Mr. Littleton is here with his cat, Trouble. It seems he shot the cat in the head to put it out of its misery. The problem is that Trouble jumped just as he pulled the trigger. The bullet hit him but not fatally. In fact, the cat ran away and has been gone for two days. He just now reappeared at home."

"Put him out of his misery from what?"

"He wouldn't tell me. He's a bit scattered right now and obviously guilt stricken about his cat. Alma's in the other exam room trying to console him."

I explained the emergency to the client who had been waiting for me and then quickly gave the vaccinations and excused myself to attend to Trouble.

Mr. Littleton was distraught. His usual neatly trimmed mustache was frazzled and two days of beard stubble covered the remainder of his face. His hands trembled as he stroked Trouble. He looked up as I entered the room and his blood-shot eyes told the story of what must have been an agonizing forty-eight hour marathon.

"Do you want to tell me what happened, Mr. Littleton?" I said as I began to survey the damage to Trouble's head.

"It's that blasted bladder. It got blocked again and I just couldn't see putting this poor cat through more surgery so I decided to end his misery. I would have done so too if it hadn't been for these damned crippled hands of mine. I put a bowl of food on the porch for him and as he was eating I put the pistol to his head and said my good-byes. He must have heard the click of the trigger hammer as I cocked the gun and he jumped. When I finally pulled the trigger, I must have grazed him because he jumped off the porch and ran through the woods.

"How did you conclude he had a bladder problem?"

"Well, that was easy enough. I've been through this enough that I can recognize the symptoms. He kept going to the litter box and didn't produce anything. Anyway, that's not important now. What is important is that he doesn't suffer anymore. I want you to finish what I was unable to do."

I had completed enough of my exam to know that Trouble's problems did not originate with a urinary obstruction. Now it was my turn to put on my hat as the cat's advocate and protect him from any rash decisions on the part of the owner. "Did it ever occur to you that he may have been constipated or that a cat with a urinary blockage would not be interested in the food you placed before him?" I was having a hard time being compassionate with the owner. This was a typical case of what happens when a pet owner takes on the task of being judge, jury and executioner.

"Couldn't be, Doc. I've been through this enough to know when a cat can't pee."

"Do you think a cat with a urinary blockage can just disappear for two days and then show up again?"

"Well… no…I guess not."

I had to temper my feelings of anger toward Mr. Littleton or Trouble would pay the penalty for my backing the owner into a corner.

"Look, Mr. Littleton, Trouble has been hurt badly. He's dehydrated, malnourished and appears to have a broken jaw and a blind eye. I'm going to take an x-ray of his head and see what we can do. You have a seat in the reception room and I'll let you know something in a few minutes."

"Okay, Doc. You go ahead and do that. I don't need to tell you that I feel rotten about all this."

Alma put the radiograph on the viewer and we both stood there in amazement that Trouble was still alive. The radiograph showed the path of the bullet. Mr. Littleton had used a small revolver that fired a low velocity .22 caliber shell. Small metal fragments and pieces of bone were deposited along the path from the .22 caliber shell wherever bone had momentarily interrupted the bullet's journey through the skull. The projectile had entered through the top of the head at a steep angle, traveled behind the left eye without entering the brain, pierced through the hard pallet and then fractured the left lower jaw on its exit. The left optic nerve had probably been severed but that was incidental considering what could have happened. I held a specimen cat skull in my palm as I tried to visualize how such a shot could have missed so many vital structures such as the carotid artery, esophagus, windpipe and jugular vein. I asked Alma to bring Mr. Littleton back so I could explain the treatment plan.

Mr. Littleton was much calmer as he joined me at the viewer screen. "I have had a good bit of time to think all this over while I was waiting, and I want to do the right thing for Trouble."

"That's good Mr. Littleton. Trouble's been a good cat and has had his share of problems. Here's what we need to do." I explained that Trouble's left eye was blind and a source of pain and infection and that we would have to remove it. The jaw could be repaired and made functional again. "God put an extra measure of healing in cats, Mr. Littleton, so I'm sure Trouble will do well. But before we can start on any of this, we need to get him hydrated and built up and bring these infections under control."

Mr. Littleton's earlier tears of distress had turned to tears of gentleness and he left the office in much better spirits than when he first arrived. Alma and I spent the next hour cleaning Trouble's wounds and installing an intravenous catheter to administer fluids and antibiotics. Trouble was cooperative throughout the whole process so we were able to do the work without causing him further discomfort. I left Trouble in Alma's capable hands and drove to Sapphire to do a presale exam on a thoroughbred mare.

Sapphire is located west of Brevard in Jackson County. It was going to take me about forty-five minutes to get to the horse stable and I was happy for that. I needed the time to settle down. When we moved to Brevard in 1977, we knew the area was blessed with some of the most beautiful mountains to be found anywhere. God must have taken a special liking to this place during creation. Transylvania County is bordered by the Pisgah National Forest on the west and the Nantahala Forest on the south. The curvy mountain roads necessitate that distance from one place to the next be measured in time not miles. I had not envisioned the need to travel outside our county when we moved here. The size of the county itself and the time to travel its unique geographical makeup would seem to exclude calls into other counties. However, large animal veterinarians are few and far between in rural areas so farm calls outside the county were common. I didn't mind the drive, especially today. The leaves on the maples and birch trees were turning and seemed to announce the splendor that was soon to arrive. The mountain scenery was soothing and by the time I arrived at the stable, I was once again in a good mood.

After I completed the examination of the mare, I decided to drive into Cashiers for lunch before returning to the office. Cashiers has a small population most of the year but during the summer months swells with vacationers who flock there to avoid the hot summers in Georgia, South Carolina and Florida. October was an "in-between" month. Its beauty in the autumn of the year would bring many tourists just to observe the leaf change. But that tourist period was usually packed into one weekend and still about ten days away, so I took my chances that there would not be any real crowds at the restaurants.

After parking the truck I strolled through the small town and found an inviting little café. Just as I was about to enter the door, I heard a voice behind me. It was C.J. The last time I saw him he was devising a plan to test his skills as an archer to tranquilize an uncooperative steer. He started talking before I had a chance to ask about his success.

"I wouldn't eat there if I were you. I was up this way visiting some friends and then decided to get some lunch. But this place… it doesn't look right."

"What do you mean it doesn't look right? It's clean, not crowded, and I can see the cook. He looks healthy."

"That's what I mean."

"What?"

"That's what I mean. My father taught me not to eat in places like that."

"Clean and not crowded?"

"You saw the cook, right?"

"So?"

"My father said, 'Son, don't ever eat in a place where the cook is skinny.' Something's wrong. There's not even a fat person working in there."

"Jay, he's just thin, that's all."

"He's not thin. He's skinny and that's a clear sign he don't like his own cooking and neither does anyone else working in there."

"Well, look Jay, on a different subject, did ya'll catch that steer?"

"Nope. That tranquilizer you sold us didn't do the job. I shot that steer myself, square in the left flank and he just kept on going. Never even slowed down."

"Did you say the left flank?"

"Yep."

"No shot's going to work there. That's where the rumen is located and all you did was put the tranquilizer in the giant portion of the stomach. Stop by the office later and pick up another dose. This time aim your arrow for the leg muscle."

"That ain't going to be too easy."

"Why's that?"

"All we have to do is look at him from a distance and he runs off."

"Well, I'm sure you and your friends can figure out something. And, oh, by the way, I think you are right."

"Right about what?"

"That cook does look skinny. I'll wait until I get back to Brevard to eat."

I parted company with C.J. and drove to Brevard and grabbed a quick sandwich before the afternoon appointments began.

My first appointment was with Mr. Palmer. Beau's face was swollen again and now had a foul odor to it. "Mr. Palmer, do you remember when I extracted the fractured tooth that I mentioned a sore on the hard palate that had me a little concerned?"

"I remember something about another area that you said looked a little peculiar."

"Well, that sore is much larger now and very irregular in appearance. I'm afraid we might be dealing with a tumor."

67

"But, it was the fall that broke his tooth. I don't understand how a fall could cause a tumor."

"The fall didn't cause a tumor. The injury to the tooth occurred because the mouth was already compromised with another problem. The fall was just coincidental. Without the fall, we would still have seen some sort of problem in his mouth. It would just have taken longer to manifest itself. I'm going to take a radiograph of Beau's mouth and get a biopsy of that growth. I will have to give a light sedative to Beau to get a good picture, but he'll be ready to pick up by 5 p.m."

"When do you think you'll know something, Doc? You know Beau's been with me ten years and is one of my good buddies," Mr. Palmer said in a casual manner as he tried to ward off some surfacing emotions.

"I know you are concerned, Mr. Palmer. The x-rays will be ready this afternoon and may provide us some information, but the biopsy will take a few days."

Alma and I positioned Beau for the radiograph and took several pictures from different angles. While Alma processed the film, I took a small amount of tissue from the tumor for the biopsy and placed it in a formalin solution.

The radiographs didn't give us a complete answer. There was a small amount of bone loss around the area where the tooth had been fractured, but that could have been due to injury itself and not related to another problem. We would have to wait for the biopsy results.

I was taking one final look at the x-rays when Susan told me I had an appointment waiting. "This one is a little strange. The client is new and has driven up from Greenville, South Carolina for you to treat her dog for mange."

"Are you kidding? Why doesn't she just have her regular veterinarian treat her dog?"

"She said she heard you had some magic treatment."

"I don't know where she heard that. The treatments for the different types of mange are pretty much standard once the type of mange is identified. Ask Alma to show her into the exam room. I haven't had a chance to look at Trouble since I returned from Sapphire. I'm going to do that first. Tell her I'll be in there in a few minutes to see if we can figure out what's going on with her dog."

"I'll show her in the exam room. Alma's still busy processing the biopsy sample."

Trouble was resting comfortably. The IV fluids had already brought brightness to his eyes and he seemed more alert. Alma had done a wonderful job cleaning the wounds and removing the caked-on blood and debris that were imbedded into the various wounds. This cat was one tough character and I knew he would come through just fine, but he had a long way to go toward recovery.

Miss Stapleton was an attractive lady in her mid thirties. She was approximately five foot eight and was very well dressed in slacks and an expensive silk blouse. With her was Rocky, a four-pound brown Chihuahua with a light sweater that matched Miss Stapleton's blue blouse. Unless the sweater hid a skin problem, mange would be way down the list of whatever problem this dog might have.

I introduced myself and took the sweater off Rocky. The dog's skin and hair coat were a personification of health. "Miss Stapleton, I hate that you made a trip from Greenville for me to look at your dog for no reason. His skin is very healthy. Why do you think he's has mange?"

"Oh, it's not him that I'm concerned about. It's me." The exam table separated us, but she still managed to get uncomfortably close as she whispered, "You see, I'm single and I own a management consulting business in Greenville. I can't have rumors being spread about me concerning this little problem I have. I've been seeing a couple different men and now I have a rash that is driving me crazy. It's right here." And with those words, she raised the right side of her blouse and pointed to a rash.

"Alma, stop whatever you are doing and come in here." I was frightened. One never knows if he is being set up for a potential lawsuit when a client acts like this. With Alma in the room I felt a little more at ease in addressing Miss Stapleton.

"Please, Miss Stapleton, lower your blouse. Frankly, I don't understand why you are seeing a veterinarian about a skin problem you have."

"It's like I said. I can't take a chance on rumors. I don't know if I got this rash from one of the men I'm dating or if it's something else entirely. If I go to one of my local doctors, and it's a problem associated with…you know…then my business could be ruined. Anyway, I want you to take a close look at it and give me your opinion."

"Miss Stapleton, a closer look won't be necessary. Let me suggest you see a friend of mine who is a physician. He's less than a

69

mile from here, and I'm sure I can get you an appointment this afternoon."

"Well, I suppose that would be okay. Is he good at diagnosing skin rashes?"

"He's a genius. I'll have Susan call him and make the appointment. By the way, may I ask how you happened to make your appointment with me?"

"Oh, that was easy. Vets are usually pretty good with skin problems so I looked up veterinarians in the phone book. Brooks is close to the beginning of the alphabet so your name was the first one listed. Did you say the physician is a 'he?'?"

"Yes, a very nice man. He, his wife and four children live just down the street from us."

"Oh…Well, that's fine. I'm sure he's good since you recommended him."

Miss Stapleton left and I never saw her or Rocky again. My physician friend told me later that her rash was a contact allergy not related to her worst fears. He referred her to a specialist…in her hometown.

CHAPTER TEN

The next week came and went quickly and with it the painful news that Beau's biopsy revealed an aggressive melanoma. Treatment for such a malignancy is really non- existent. Surgery on the upper jaw would be useless since the tumor had been so invasive as to grow across most of the hard palate. Chemotherapy and radiation had little promise on such a tumor and, at ten years old, Beau's age was not in his favor. He was already demonstrating arthritic problems and having difficulty moving about. Chances are his inability to coordinate his arthritic body precipitated the fall from the retaining wall.

I had called Mr. Palmer and told him the sad news. We discussed the options and he came to the conclusion that humane euthanasia was the most compassionate choice. Later in the week Mr. Palmer brought Beau to the office where Susan, Alma, Mr. Palmer, and I gathered around and petted Beau as we said our final good-byes. The tumor had grown horribly and was a hideous site. But we didn't have to see that. As long as we didn't open his mouth, it was as if everything was fine. Except for Beau's weight loss, he appeared to be the same sweet Lab we had all grown to love over the years. His wagging tail would still knock any unguarded object from a table, and his willingness to please was undaunted. But we all knew it was time. Walking was now a difficult chore, and he had lost his appetite. When he did manage to take in a few bites, his mouth would bleed.

Even with the obvious staring us in the face we were having difficulty in carrying through with the procedure. Euthanasia is always tough and veterinarians don't approach such a final act without agonizing over the decision. After what appeared to be a long time of silence, Mr. Palmer nodded his head for me to proceed with the injection. As the solution entered Beau's vein, I could feel his body go limp as he slipped into unconsciousness. Death came a few seconds later. Mr. Palmer and I consoled each other. It was a cheerless time. Alma pulled both of us from our despair with reminders of Beau in his youthful days, and she lifted our spirits about the hard choice we had just made on Beau's behalf.

Two events had punctuated the week: Beau's cancer and euthanasia and Mr. Littleton's rash act to terminate his cat's "misery," as he put it. Trouble had responded well to rehydration and antibiotics so we had proceeded with surgery. I removed the left eye and repaired his fractured jaw. That was the easy part. Dealing with Mr. Littleton and his guilt was another whole issue. I did what I could to console and redirect his focus about how well Trouble was doing. His previous urinary tract surgery was doing its job and should cause him no further problems. I then emphasized that Trouble would be able to eat normally with his repaired jaw and that he should live out a normal life. All that seemed to fall on deaf ears. Everything else for the week had fallen into a normal pattern except for a 3:30 a.m. calf delivery on Wednesday. The week had been long and emotionally arduous.

An uplifting of my spirits was in order, and I knew exactly where to find it. I would see Jack Williams, the cobbler. Jack's shop was in the center of town in a portion of the old McMinn Building. I had been in the building dozens of times but on this occasion the plaque on the face of the building caught my attention. The building had been erected in 1899! I had studied Brevard's history but for some reason, as I stood before the building this time, the history now came alive. I tried to visualize the McMinn Building and its participation in Brevard's growth after it became the county seat.

Even though Brevard had become Transylvania's county seat in 1881, the town sat somewhat dormant until 1892 when several independent forces converged and jerked Brevard into the twentieth century. George Vanderbilt saw the beauty of this region's mountains and decided to build his palatial and now famous Biltmore House. To insure privacy and the grandeur that the largest private residence in the United States should enjoy, he purchased over 100,000 acres of land that spanned the distance from Asheville to Brevard. This endeavor created a massive number of jobs. Laborers of all sorts flocked to the area for employment. The lumber needed for both local and regional needs prompted the development of the logging industry. The completion of the rail line connecting Hendersonville to Brevard in 1895 assured the success of this little town known as Brevard. Now, with the convenience of satisfactory roads and the railroad, tourism began to blossom. The Toxaway Company established itself as a developer of resorts in Transylvania County and adjacent Jackson County. Brevard was booming. Now, there was a need for a commercial downtown area to focus the business aspects of all this developmental activity that had happened in the previous eight years.

This need was met with the completion of the McMinn Building in 1899, and this is where our story begins.

The two-story McMinn Building was the first commercial brick building in Brevard and, appropriately, occupied the prime corner address of West Main and Broad Streets. I must have looked like a tourist as I backed away from the building a bit and studied its late Victorian architecture. Since its erection various parts of the building had housed an assortment of businesses. The Brevard Banking Company, The Transylvania Railroad Company, pharmacies, groceries, a restaurant, a department store and various professional businesses had all enjoyed this wonderful old building. "This building is gorgeous," I thought. Pillars on the Main Street side highlighted the corbelled brickwork and cast-iron storefront. I wondered if the original architects had ever envisioned that one day a shoe repair shop would occupy one of the storefronts.

Hanging from the soffit over the entrance to Jack's store was his sign, a huge three-dimensional replica of a high-top black shoe with the slogan "We Save Soles." As I entered the store through two large double doors, I felt like I had been immediately transported back fifty years. The aroma of leather and shoe polish permeated the air. The distance from the store entrance to the service counter was at least forty-five feet. The enormous size of the store was not necessitated by Jack's business. It was just there, and its fifteen-foot ceilings accented the obvious disproportion of the store's size to the number of shoes needing repair in Brevard.

Jack was at the counter servicing a customer and talking in a loud and animated way to overcome the noisy leather stitching machines in the background. I looked at the decorations Jack had used in an attempt to fill the mammoth size of his store. Jack had a strong Cherokee Indian heritage so much of the decor reflected that part of his background. On the left wall was a large painting of an Indian chief in full-feathered regalia headdress. Under the painting on a small table were a few Indian artifacts: a tomahawk, a few arrowheads and some flint rocks, and adjacent to the table were three cured rattlesnake skins nailed to a piece of plywood. Next to all this was an isolated glass showcase that contained a few tins of shoe polish, shoe laces and assorted other shoe care products. There were no special lights to accentuate the displays. Only the four large, ball-type fixtures that had come with the inception of the modern convenience of electricity illuminated the interior. The original pine floors with eighty years of wear didn't do much to reflect the light. Jack had obviously never taken a course in merchandizing and wasn't particularly interested in equipping for the modern age. Nevertheless, his business did well.

On the right wall was another showcase that displayed a few pairs of handmade moccasins, shoelaces, a few leather wallets for men and two women's leather pocket- books. Next to the display case was an upright piano and a vintage Gibson guitar on a stand. Jack saw me looking at the guitar. "Be with you in a minute, Doc. Grab that guitar and strum a few chords." Jack finished dealing with the customer and another man took his place in line and stepped to the counter. Jack grabbed the shoes given to him and hastily gave the man a receipt. I couldn't hear exactly what Jack said but it was something to the effect, "I won't be able to start on these until tomorrow."

The customer turned around and surveyed the store and saw no other customers. "It's a very simple repair. I don't see why you can't do it right now."

"Just can't. I'm too busy. Now if you'll excuse me." Jack sashayed around the counter, brushed right by the man and hobbled to the piano. He pulled up the piano stool and situated himself with his right leg fully extended on the base pedal. He pulled the heavy leather apron above his knees to free up his legs and looked at me with a smile that would bring jubilation to a mortician. "Do you know *My Country Girl?* It's in G. I recorded this in the late '50s. You'll catch on to the tune. Just join in when you've got it."

Jack's happiness, when he was in his music, was infectious. The look of sheer joy on his face as he sang his song put a sudden and definite end to my gloominess. His face just made a person happy to look at him. It was one of character, weather worn and reflecting definite bone structure of his Indian heritage. I figured Jack to have been born somewhere around 1930. As he sang his song he began to animate the rhythm by moving his head side to side, tossing his long crimson-colored hair in all directions. His stubby, shoe polish stained fingers streaked across the keys with ease as he sang the chorus. Even at sixty-plus years his voice was powerful and enjoyable. Jack's eyes were sparkling as he became totally engrossed in the song.

I was beginning to catch the song's pattern and chord changes when I heard a voice from the middle of the room. It was the man Jack had told "I'm too busy."

The man blurted out in exasperation, "Mr. Williams, when will my shoes be ready?"

It was as if the man had unplugged a power supply. The piano stopped right in the middle of a measure and Jack's phrasing stopped mid-syllable. His facial pattern turned from sheer joy to utter surprise. I could almost read his thoughts, "Can't the man see I'm singing?"

Jack spun around on the piano bench. "They'll be ready next Tuesday." He assumed his position and took up the song in mid-verse exactly where he had been interrupted. Then just as suddenly he swung around again as the man was completing his long journey to the front door and said with a smile on his face, "Make that next Friday." The customer made his way to the door and jerked it open and left.

"Now, where were we? Ah, yes, the third verse, I believe."

Jack and I had a great time playing the country and western songs he had recorded some thirty years ago. He pulled out a piece of sheet music with his picture on the front, "This one was in the Top 10."

I looked at my watch. "Oh, my gosh, we were having such a good time I lost track of the time. I better get back to the office."

"Yeah, I guess I had better get back to mine, too. Drop in again and don't make yourself so scarce. We'll stir up some more oldies. Better bundle up…the temperature's dropping."

Susan greeted me as I returned to the office. "You won't believe what you have as your next patient. Care to guess?"

"No telling. Let's see, we've already had a guinea pig, a cat, a dog and a ferret this morning so it must be something a little different."

"It's in the first exam room waiting for you…in a bowl."

As I entered the room the young lady said, "Thank you, Dr. Brooks, for rushing back from lunch. I know you have a busy schedule and I appreciate your seeing Luey."

I was glad I didn't have to explain that my schedule was busy today, not because of all the clients I had seen, but because of my side-track visit to Jack's place. The client gave me the reasons for her visit. Somehow, Luey the turtle had escaped from his bowl and had fallen off the edge of the table and next to a piece of flypaper on the floor.

"I guess Luey couldn't help himself. The temptation was too great with all the flies, gnats and other bugs stuck in the trap. When I found him, he was stuck as good as you please right in the middle of the trap with a half-eaten fly in his mouth. The fly was stuck in his mouth, his mouth was stuck together, and his shell was stuck to the paste."

"Do you know if this fly paper is toxic?"

"It's not supposed to be, but I'm not sure at this point."

We called the store and learned the paper was made of a nontoxic material and could be removed with vegetable oil. I pulled my stool to the exam table and put on my magnifying glasses. Luey, weighing no more than a quarter ounce, was the smallest patient I had seen and removing the paste was going to be a tedious job. Fortunately the paste was removed with relative ease and Luey was no worse for his adventure. Luey reminded me of what I loved so much about my job -- the variety. I really didn't know what the next client might present. There were surprises awaiting me most every day.

I finished up the afternoon appointments and left the office early, excited that I would have a long quiet evening at home. Just as I was reaching for the handle on the front door of my house, the door swung open with Linda on the other side. "Thank goodness you are home. I've called the office, the coffee shop - everywhere looking for you."

"I just left the office and went to the gas station. What's so urgent?"

"We need a wet nurse mouse and we need one quick!" she said as she spun around and called to Travis, "It's going be okay, your dad's home and he'll fix everything." Linda turned back to me. "Here's what happened. You know that little mouse we got Travis two weeks ago…well, she died in labor this afternoon, poor thing, but not before she delivered eight babies. So, I figure all we need to do is find another mouse that has milk."

Linda, with her perpetual optimism, saw absolutely no problem finding a replacement mouse. She was right in one thing, the young ones, still hairless and too small to rear by hand, had no chance at all without a mother mouse. But we lived in a small town which had no pet store at that time, and I didn't know anyone who had a mouse.

"Has Travis tried his friends?"

"Yes, and they all have hamsters, guinea pigs, gerbils, you name it, gold fish, but no one has a mouse."

"Well, honey, it's a shame, but it really looks rather hopeless, don't you think?"

"Wait…wait…I've got it!" Linda darted from the room with Travis right on her heels.

Not knowing what might happen next, I sat down and waited. Five minutes later Linda and Travis reappeared. Both their faces were beaming.

"We found one and she's only sixteen miles away."

"Found what?"

"A wet nurse mouse, of course."

"Incredible," I thought. Linda's determination had once again prevailed. She related what had happened. It seems her hairdresser had mentioned a couple months ago that her aunt had a pet mouse and although she wasn't sure, she thought it might be a female. A couple of telephone calls confirmed this "aunt" did have a female mouse which had, in fact, just lost its young. Linda convinced the lady that she had a mother mouse without any young and that we had a litter of mice without a mother. A deal was struck to borrow the "wet nurse" for three weeks.

"God provided this little mother mouse. I told Travis to pray about it and, see…isn't that just wonderful. Now, if I can just find my car keys, we'll go get Hilda."

"Hilda?"

"That's her name, and if I might say so, it's a very popular name right now."

So Linda and Travis left on their journey to get Hilda. I was charged with the duty of keeping the little babies warm until their return. When they returned, the new mother went right to her duty station with the built-in instinct to care for the little ones.

It's been five weeks now since that crisis and we have eight, healthy mice. We also have Hilda as a permanent resident. The aunt thought the mouse had adapted so well to our household that she should just stay indefinitely. Brevard's a small town and homes for mice are a bit difficult to find. Linda is going to the hairdresser tomorrow. Who knows? There might be hope.

CHAPTER ELEVEN

Seven months had passed since that first visit with Mr. Owenby and I had almost forgotten about his cow until a shouting voice on the other end of the telephone blasted me into reality.

"Doc, it's Rosie. She ain't doing very well, and I think you best come and have a look at her."

I obtained a quick history from Mr. Owenby and knew his concern was genuine. It seemed that Rosie had steadily improved after her displaced abomasum problem in the early spring and then gained a considerable amount of weight. A weight gain, in fact, that would be quite unusual for a cow her age. My suspicions grew and I feared the worst for the old gentleman and his aging cow.

Mr. Owenby's farm was just a short drive from the office, and barring any road problems from last night's freezing rain, the drive shouldn't take more than fifteen minutes. The cold had come early this year so I took a few minutes to prepare for the weather. I pulled on my boots over an extra pair of wool socks. Farm calls can be vigorous, but most of the work is upper body and the feet can become miserably cold. I had once even gone to the expense of buying a pair of electric socks that had built-in heating coils powered by two D-size batteries. The second time I wore them was the last. I guess the wool had frayed or something because no sooner did I pull the rubber boots over them, than there was a short circuit. At first there was just a short, little twitch, a warning you might say. But I didn't pay it much attention. Then there was a stronger, steady electrical shock that sent me dancing through the office like one of those Irish tap dancers. Alma and Susan were bent over double laughing as I made frantic attempts to pull off the boots and remove the socks. After an eternal ten seconds, I removed the boots and the cursed socks. Almost ceremoniously I deposited the socks and the batteries into the waste bucket. That was the last attempt at heating my feet. Now, I just wore one or two pairs of good quality wool insulated socks.

The ride to the farm was dreary. The low-level cloud overcast was threatening more unpleasant weather, and the leafless trees with their broken limbs from the freezing rain added more drab emphasis that winter had arrived. As I approached the barn, Clarence's bent frame was standing over Rosie as she lay prostrate on a shallow bank. Clarence had done what he could to lessen her discomfort. He had stacked hay bales around Rosie to shield her from the biting wind and, as much as possible, had stuffed some hay underneath her. He had draped a blanket over her and cushioned her head with a doubled-up empty feed bag. She looked terrible and he looked pitiful. Some of the farmers in the area were all business. If a cow didn't produce, the answer was simple. She was sent to the sale barn where the outcome was always certain. Clarence was different. This cow was a friend, a companion that shared part of his every day with him. Taking care of her gave him a little work to do each day and reminded him that he was still capable of tending to his animals. The exam proved what I had feared on my first visit back in March. The bull across the river that separated the two farms had found nature's calling stronger than the river's current.

"She's in an advanced pregnancy Mr. Owenby and that has caused a terrible problem with her stomach." Clarence was stone still. At first, I thought my news had overwhelmed him. Then I realized he just hadn't heard me.

"Well, Doc, what have you got to say about her?"

"I'm going to give her some injections and an IV to see if we can pull her out of this, but I fear we are going to lose her." I don't know who felt worse, Mr. Owenby or me. This Rosie was more than just a cow to the old farmer. She reminded him of his earlier years as a dairy farmer, of better times gone by, and the loss of her would dry up a lot of pleasant memories. Clarence didn't say a word but instead hobbled to the barn and sat on a bale of Rosie's hay.

After I finished the treatments, I told the forlorn gentleman that I'd be back in a couple hours to check on her condition. Throughout the remaining morning farm calls, I kept thinking of the man and his cow and how to break the news that Rosie had a very poor chance, at best, to recover from her plight.

My return found Clarence still sitting on the hay bale. He had modified his position only slightly from when I left him two hours earlier. A heavy wool blanket engulfed his body and the top of his head. Rosie had not moved, but I did notice another blanket on her and an extension cord protruding from the blanket and extending into the barn. Clarence had taken his small heating pad and placed it on his cow. I was stiff and chilled to the bone from being exposed all morning while on an assortment of farm calls, yet Clarence seemed perfectly comfortable as he watched patiently over his cow. Rosie's condition had deteriorated. Her temperature had dropped three degrees below normal and her lungs were now congested. Breaking bad news to people about their animals is always an unpleasant chore but yelling out the verdict just seemed to add to the misery. I positioned myself close to this left ear. I didn't want to have to say this more than once. "Clarence, she's been a good cow, but I'm afraid she's not going to recover from this."

"I understand. She's not painful, is she?"

"No, she's just slipping away."

"In that case, Doc, I think I'll just sit here with her. Maybe, I can get that old kerosene heater working to warm her up a bit. I don't believe the heating pad is doing much for her. Much obliged for all your help."

As I gathered my things, Clarence was stroking Rosie's head and administering water to her through an old chicken-basting bulb. I don't believe an artist could paint a sadder scene than the one I was leaving.

After the afternoon appointments, I went home and collapsed on the sofa.

"Tough day, honey?" Linda said as she moved the footstool close to the sofa and propped up my feet.

"It was. You don't think I could talk you into a foot rub, do you?"

"Maybe later when the boys are asleep. Right now, I'm putting the finishing touches on your favorite dinner…country fried steak."

Just about that time the phone rang. The aroma of the steak dinner sashayed under my nose as I went through the dining room to answer the call.

"She's down and won't get up." That was all that was said, not who he was or even "Hello, how are you?"…or even "Sorry to call at dinnertime." But the caller didn't really need identification. It was Otis Odum. I had treated his cow Sadie just a few days ago.

"Who's down? Is it Sadie?"

"No, no, no…No, Doc. You fixed her the other day. She's adoin' just fine. This here one calved yestedee and spilled out her calf bed."

"Blasted!" I thought. A prolapsed uterus and right at dinnertime. "How long has she been down?"

"'Bout eight hours."

"Eight hours! Otis you should have called sooner."

"I tried. Your phone's been busy."

"Well, never mind. I'll be right out."

I put the phone down and looked at Linda with a look of defeat on my face. I knew she was disappointed too since she had labored on the special dinner, but with her usual perkiness she tossed me an apple. "This will ward off the hunger pains until you get back."

I devoured that apple. It was one of those good yellow ones, and I took my last bite of it just as I pulled up to the barn. The dilapidated barn was a patchwork of replacement planks and cardboard. Just about anything you can imagine had been used to plug gaping holes in the side of the barn. Old feed sacks, rusted tin roofing, and a bent up highway STOP sign were nailed wherever needed. Wilber Odum, the eldest son, sloshed his way through the mud and manure and met me at the truck just as I disposed of the apple core on the floorboard.

"Hand that core to me, Doc, and I'll throw it away for you."

Just as I was reaching for it, Mrs. Odum saw what was happening, and being a frugal woman, chastised her son. "Don't be wasteful, son. The vetinary probably got chickens at home who'd loved to finish off that core."

Who was I to argue as I dropped the core back to the floor, especially with a mountain woman of Mrs. Odum's stature? She sported a vintage World War II leather army aviator's headgear, the type with the built-in earphones. She talked from the side of her mouth that didn't have the snuff drippings. She was tough and weatherworn with a skin that wasn't much different than the leather helmet she wore, except it was a lighter shade. I couldn't help but admire that hat. She was toasty warm and I was freezing. The coldness of the day had just turned bitter after the sun had set, and I was miserable. In my haste to leave the house I had forgotten my hat and my wool socks.

Mr. Odum was lying in the mire in a contorted position next to the cow pushing on the prolapsed uterus with all his might in an attempt to replace it. But his efforts were wasted since the cow was also bloated. It was heartwarming to see a man so dedicated at saving his cow's life, but I wasn't envious of his position on the cold ground because I knew I would soon have to join him. When he saw me, he overcame his arthritis and pushed himself up. His smile stretched from ear to ear and sort of framed his huge nose, which extended from his face like a large proboscis. As he hobbled toward me to explain the situation, I marveled at his coat. It, too, was straight from World War

II. He sported an ankle-long olive drab wool trench coat. Where the buttons had once been was baling twine in precisely tied slipknots.

Mr. Odum gave me more history than anyone could ever want to hear about how the cow got into her present condition. He failed to mention malnutrition as a major cause and blamed the entire problem on his neighbor's bull. "I've been pushing on that calf bed for three hours and just having an awful time getting it to stay in. Every time I think I got it back in, it just comes out again."

As he talked, I shaved a four-inch area of hair on the cow's upper left flank. "She's bloated and all that gas in the stomach doesn't leave much room for the uterus. We'll have to get rid of the gas first." I grabbed the soap and cleaned the skin and injected ten cc's of lidocaine to anesthetize the area.

"Otis, you might want to step back a little for this next step. The smell's not very appetizing."

"Won't affect my appetite none, Doc. I ate an early dinner 'cause I thought this cow might need tending to tonight."

Like salt in a wound. I was starving… he was full. He was anticipating a problem tonight while I was looking forward to a restful evening and country fried steak. I was freezing… he wore a wool trench coat. Concentration on the procedure, though, was replacing my discomfort. I went to my bag and grabbed a scalpel and rumen trocar. As I grabbed the simple instrument, I thought about the many times I had used it and what a wonderful little contraption it was.

I made a quick incision and then plunged the trocar into the distended rumen. The methane gas escaped from the thirty-five gallon stomach compartment with a loud hissing sound.

Otis jumped up. "What's that hissing sound?"

"Methane gas."

"Dangerous?"

"Not unless you light a match to it."

"That explains it then."

"Explains what?"

"You know Claude down in the gap, don't you?"

I nodded.

"He had to do that emergency gas release sort of like what you just did a couple months ago. Not as neat though. He used a knife."

"And…?"

"Claude said, 'Just for fun, Otis, I'm agoin' test this here gas with a match.'"

"He said what?!!"

82

"You know, test it with a match."

"You let him do that?"

"Well, you know Claude when he gets a right mind to do something."

"Is he okay?"

"He is, the barn ain't."

"What happened?"

"The gas lit up like up like one of them flame throwers you see in a war movie... shooting fire ten feet outward from her side. Hotter than the Fourth of July, it was. Scared the old cow so bad she broke out the stanchion and ran down the barn's gangway torching everything as she went."

"Did Claude lose the barn?"

"No, but it is scorched a right bit."

"How about the cow?"

"Smart cow. She ran straight for the pond and jumped in."

"Gracious, Otis, that's quite a story."

"Yep, I was there. Saw the whole thing. Claude said he's through testing cow gas."

Otis and I spent the next thirty minutes cleaning the uterus. It had not swollen too much so its replacement was not difficult. I put two large antibiotic tablets into the uterus and then pulled myself up from the cold ground. Once I was up and through with the physical work, the cold returned. I was anxious to explain the cow's care and get home to a warm bath and dinner. "Well, Otis, let's talk about your cow. She'll get up in the next hour or so and when she does, move her to a dry area. Keep those blankets on her tonight. She should be back to herself by tomorrow."

"Thanks, Doc. Oh, the missus has something for you."

"I've been saving him for a special occasion, and I reckon this here is it." In her hands, which were extended straight towards me, was a rooster. "You saved our cow, Sadie, a few days back, and this day, you've done saved Millie. I figure a life for a life you might say. So here's Ralph to do with as you please. You could stew him if you want, but I suppose he probably could be obliging to your hens."

Her method of payment was a sacrifice, and I didn't have the heart to tell her I lived in a residential section of town and not on a farm with chickens. She was way ahead of my flimsy excuses about not having a way to carry Ralph home.

"Here's a box to put Ralph in until you get back to your farm." She crammed the rooster into a shallow orange crate and placed it on the front seat of the truck. "And, he's real reliable."

"Reliable?"

"He gives his first crowing at four in the morning...just in time for you to milk the cows before you go to your vetinary job."

As I drove out the gravel drive to the main road, Ralph must have felt the need to practice for tomorrow morning's performance. He let out some of the loudest hackles I had ever heard. With the windows closed to the cold, the sound reverberated throughout the truck with a painful deafening noise. "I'll freeze to death if I lower the windows. I'll just endure." Then I saw it. The apple core. He'll quiet down if he has the remains of that apple. I pulled over and stopped the truck, lifted the lid on the orange crate with one hand, and grabbed for Ralph with the other to keep him from escaping. I wasn't quick enough. Ralph had had it with the box and flew the coup. I've never seen a chicken move so fast. I grabbed one of his feet and he reached down and nailed me with his beak. I grabbed one of his wings and he beat me into submission with his other wing. The truck cab was filling up with feathers when I finally landed both hands around his scrawny little neck. He put both sets of his claws on my wrists.

The action stopped as fast as it had begun. We were at a stalemate. I had him by the neck and he had me by the wrist. And then, just as if fate had control over both his eyes and mine, we jointly starred at the apple core on the floorboard. I looked at his eyes. They were fixed on the apple core and he seemed mesmerized by it. Ever so carefully I released my left hand from his neck and reached for the apple core. I placed it in his box. Ralph, with those little beady eyes of his, jumped in after it. I slammed the lid and just held it closed for a moment as I caught my breath and contemplated how long Ralph had before he landed in the stew pot.

My trip home took me by Carl Whitehurst's farm. He had a bunch of chickens. Maybe he would take Ralph off my hands. As luck would have it, Carl was home and was happy to have Ralph. He had just lost his rooster to a red-tailed hawk. Carl put Ralph in the chicken lot and we watched as he strutted the limits of the confinement and then disappeared into the hen house. So, as quickly as I had come to know Ralph, we parted company. I felt relieved as I drove away, but somehow I couldn't help but feel sorry for the hawk.

CHAPTER TWELVE

The alarm jolted me into consciousness at six-thirty. On any other morning I could have rolled from the bed and started the day with as much ease as one can muster before daybreak. But not this morning. Even though I knew it would be but a brief deferment of the inevitable, I struggled for the alarm clock and pressed the snooze alarm. Then I turned over and snuggled with Linda. The call the night before at the Odum's farm had chilled me to the bone and left me near exhaustion. The altercation with Ralph consumed what little energy that had remained. Even the hot shower before bed did not have its usual calming effect so the night's sleep had not been restful. As I began to drift into the twilight stage that narrowly separates sleep from wakefulness, the alarm sounded again. I could hear the boys rumbling around getting ready for school. "No rest for the weary," I thought. A hot cup of coffee and the chill of the late November morning air would rejuvenate me.

My body must have been engaged in slow motion. By the time I got to the breakfast table, the boys had finished eating and were putting on their coats. A quick hug and they were out the door to catch the school bus.

"They seem to be moving right smartly this morning," I said.

Linda brought me some coffee as she sat down at the table. "They missed the bus yesterday and didn't enjoy the cold walk to school."

"I tell you, last night was a doosey." I related the events of the night before, culminating in the fracas with Ralph. If it hadn't been for the good graces of Carl Whitehurst, we would be having chicken for dinner tonight."

"I was wondering what those feathers were on your clothes."

"Oh, no!" I said as I stood up from the table.

"What is it, honey?"

"It was so dark when I got in last night, I didn't even notice if there were feathers in the truck."

"If your shirt, pants and socks are any indication, I would say you could count on it."

I poured the remainder of the coffee down my throat, grabbed the vacuum cleaner from the utility room, and went to the truck. It was worse than I thought. Feathers everywhere and something I hadn't counted on…rooster droppings on the seat, dash, floor, sun visor and armrest. "Thank goodness for vacuum cleaners," I thought as I reached into every crevice of the truck cab. A little soap and water removed the other part. There wasn't much I could do about the tear in the seat where Ralph had hooked one of his spurs. I was thankful the tear was in the seat and not my arm. Feeling good about the quick and thorough cleaning job I had accomplished, I put away the vacuum cleaner.

"Were you able to get all the feathers?"

"It was a snap with the vacuum." I kissed Linda good-bye and jumped in the truck.

About a mile away from the house, the inefficiencies of my feather cleaning became abundantly clear to me when I turned on the heater fan. In the microsecond it takes electricity to travel the short distance from the switch to the fan, the truck was filled with feathers. "Blast that rooster," was all I could muster as I lowered the windows to let out some of the debris. "I just hope the hawk at Carl's place has reinforcements."

When I arrived at the office parking lot, feathers were everywhere. The inside of the truck looked like the aftermath of a pillow fight with feathers scattered from ceiling to floor. I jumped from the truck and gave my clothes a quick brushing before entering the back door of the clinic. "There, that should have it," I thought. "None the worse for wear."

Susan and Alma were both at the reception desk as I entered. "Good morning, ladies."

Alma said a quick good morning and then covered her mouth and went laughing from the room.

"What's with her?"

Susan was about the same but managed to fight back the laughter long enough to motion me to an area outside hearing distance of the reception room. "Oh, it's nothing much except we're not used to…to seeing you…" It was almost shameful to see someone fight back the laughter that way. Susan was wiping away tears with a tissue she was laughing so hard. "…to seeing you with feathers in your hair." I darted to the rest room and looked in the mirror. I didn't think it was so funny. Feathers were tangled in my hair and caught underneath my collar and in some other places that one might say were…well, inappropriate. I closed the door and pulled a set of surgical scrubs from the closet.

Alma and Susan were still laughing when I came from the rest room. They had put both phones on hold until, as they later told me, they regained their composure. "I'll tell ya'll all about it later, but do you suppose we could start the day now with a little briefing as to what is on the schedule?"

Susan was first to regain her poise and told me why she had motioned me away from the reception room. "Mrs. Galloway came in early this morning with Barney, and I didn't want her to see us laughing since she is quite concerned about the way Barney is breathing."

"Alma, take her right to the exam room."

I gathered my stethoscope and went straight to the exam room and greeted Mrs. Galloway. "Good morning, Mrs. Galloway. Susan tells me that Barney is having some difficulty catching his breath."

In her very gentle and soft-spoken manner, Mrs. Galloway began to provide me with a history of Barney's current problem. "Right now, he's doing real good. His breathing looks almost normal, but over the past couple weeks, I've noticed that the least amount of exercise leaves him panting and almost at the point of collapse. I'm very concerned he has something serious taking place in his little body."

Barney was a black schnauzer that weighed about twenty-two pounds. Even at rest on the exam table there were some notable abnormalities that concerned me. Little Barney's neck was so extended that his head appeared to be just a continuation of it instead of a distinct and separate part of his anatomy. His respirations were short and about double the normal rate. His eyes were alert yet had a wearisome cast. I put my stethoscope to his chest and could hear only faint, muffled heart sounds. This wasn't good. I placed the stethoscope on the table and told Mrs. Galloway of my suspicions.

"We will need an x-ray to see for sure, but I'm concerned that when that car hit Barney last year and broke his leg that he may have also suffered an injury to the chest. His respiration and heart sounds are muffled and that usually means something is blocking the sounds that I can normally hear."

"What do you mean 'blocking the sounds'??" "

"Usually, sounds in the chest transfer very well to the stethoscope. The lungs pretty much fill the chest cavity and surround the heart so there is little to no interference in hearing the heart. However, in Barney's case, I can barely hear the heart. That tells me something other than normal lung tissue is in his chest. Now, exactly what that is, I can't say for sure without an x-ray but I fear we may be dealing with a diaphragmatic hernia."

Mrs. Galloway was stroking Barney's head. "What exactly is a diaphrag…what did you call it?"

"I probably spoke too soon. Let's take the x-ray and then we'll be better able to determine what the next step will be."

Barney became immediately anxious when Alma and I entered the x-ray room. He was already stressed and when the two of us, draped in our lead-lined gloves and aprons, began to place him in an uncomfortable position to get the x-ray, he began to panic. His gum color changed from pink to blue as we placed him on his left side for the picture. He began to pant and struggled to breathe. "Just a minute, Alma. Let's give him some oxygen and then try again." We fitted a loose mask over Barney's muzzle, eased him on his side and took the picture. Alma developed the film and our fears were confirmed. Barney did have a diaphragmatic hernia. I asked Alma to put Barney in the hospital ward and then returned to the exam room and sat down next to Mrs. Galloway as I gave her the news.

"Mrs. Galloway, I'm afraid Barney has what I feared…a diaphragmatic hernia. This is a serious problem and the only possible remedy requires surgery." I pulled out a pen and piece of paper and drew a picture of the problem as I described it to her. "I'm not much of an artist but let me try to explain this to you. The diaphragm is a thin muscle that separates the chest from the abdominal area. When we take a breath, the diaphragm expands and pulls air into the lungs. When we exhale the diaphragm relaxes and allows the air to be expelled. I know this sounds elementary, but it is important to understanding the problem."

"Please don't apologize. I need to understand this so I can explain it to my husband."

"In Barney's case, there is a rip in the diaphragm which has allowed some of the organs that are normally in the abdomen to move into the chest cavity. This means Barney's lungs can't expand to their full capacity. And without an intact diaphragm, he can't inhale. His abdominal muscles are really straining to pull air into the chest.

"Oh, my goodness, but I guess that explains why he has so much difficulty breathing."

"Exactly. Barney probably had damage to the diaphragm when the car hit him last year. The x-ray taken at that time didn't show a hernia, but I suspect there was a small rent in the diaphragm that slowly enlarged until it was large enough to permit the liver, stomach or some of the intestinal tract to slip into the chest."

"What do we do now? Can Barney's diaphragm be fixed?"

"I wouldn't be honest with you if I didn't tell you the surgery is difficult and full of potential problems. Our first hurdle in the repair is the anesthesia. You see, the moment we make our incision, Barney will no longer be able to breathe on his own. The abdominal muscles that were functioning as a backup to his diaphragm will be unable to pull against the torn diaphragm. That means we will have to breathe for him."

"How can you do that? I don't understand."

"Barney will be placed on gas anesthesia. When we do that we put a tube down the windpipe so we can deliver the exact amount of anesthetic we want. Then we will delegate one person whose sole duty is to provide anesthesia. She will watch all the vital signs and use the anesthetic bag to expand Barney's lungs. The repair will then consist of removing the abdominal organs from the chest, placing them back in their proper place, and then closing the defect in the diaphragm. Anywhere during this process, we could encounter problems."

"Could Barney die?"

"We won't have a full assessment of the damage to Barney's chest and abdomen until we are in surgery, but yes, there is a possibility that Barney may not survive the procedure."

Mrs. Galloway paused for just a moment and then said, "I'm sure my husband would want us to go ahead with the surgery, but I feel I should call him first. Is there anything else you need to do before Barney's surgery?"

"We need to do some bloodwork."

"Go ahead and do that while I call my husband."

An hour later we were in surgery. Mr. Galloway agreed with his wife to proceed with the surgery, the blood chemistry tests were within normal limits and Susan had freed up the schedule by moving all the morning appointments to the afternoon. Alma and I were gowned in and ready to start. I made a ten-inch incision beginning at Barney's sternum and ending just a little past the belly button. The liver, part of the small intestine and the stomach had all moved from their proper place in the abdominal cavity and were now occupying part of the chest. Alma was seated next to the anesthesia machine and was doing the breathing for Barney by slowly inflating the anesthetic bag and then making a sudden release. As I began to reposition the misplaced organs, I could see the pink lungs expanding and contracting. The heart monitor was steady and all appeared to be going well. It was only after I got everything back in place that I noticed the horror that is sometimes discovered only at surgery. Radiographs are valuable, but once in a while they reveal only a portion of the total picture. And that was exactly what had happened in this case.

"Alma, do only a partial inflation. Something's not right here."

I shifted the liver to the right and then to the left. "We've got a problem." I pulled my hands from the incision and must have had a look of pure dread on my face.

"What is it?" Alma asked as she continued with the manual respiration.

"Only half the diaphragm is here. There's about a one-half inch remnant down the right rib cage, but basically there is no diaphragm on the right side. It must have atrophied from lack of use."

"What are you going to do?"

"I'm not sure yet. This is a total surprise. I expected to see a defect that could be sutured, not the absence of such a large portion of the diaphragm. We don't have the implantable mesh, and even if we did, I don't believe we could depend on it holding with a defect this size."

I pondered the predicament. If we closed the surgical incision without making a repair, we would have to hope Barney could hold his own while the Galloways took him to a veterinary teaching hospital about three hours away. There were no facilities any closer at that time that would have the mesh…not a promising alternative. I told myself to think "outside the box." All the methods I had learned in school and in practice would not solve this problem. No reason to continue thinking along those lines. Then I remembered a book I had read just a few weeks earlier. I had always had an interest in reconstructive surgery. Knowing my interest, a friend of mine, who was a general surgeon at the local hospital, had loaned such a book to me. Little did I know just a few weeks later how valuable that book would be. It didn't describe how to solve my present dilemma, but it did open my mind to a possible technique. I just had to be bold enough to attempt it.

The diaphragm is nothing more that a muscle. So, what I needed was a muscle to replace the one that was missing. The reconstructive surgical book had detailed techniques to cover skin defects with what are called "rotating flaps". There's more to the procedure than described here, but basically, this is a method where normal, undamaged skin is moved from a healthy site to cover a defect in an adjacent area where skin is missing. I concluded that the same technique could be used to cover a muscle defect. It would be of the utmost importance to maintain a viable blood supply to any muscle that I might move to replace the diaphragm. If the blood supply feeding the rotated muscle was damaged and failed to function, the muscle would die and the procedure would fail. I decided the long abdominal muscle running down the right side of the body was of sufficient size in both length and width to accomplish the job. I estimated the length of muscle needed for the diaphragm. Some length would be lost when I folded it back and sutured it to the left side of the diaphragm so I had to allow for that. I knew this was an all or nothing solution – once the procedure was started there was no reasonable course of reversal.

With some fear and trepidation, I made the ten-inch incision down the midline of the muscle. I then cut across the muscle and continued the incision back toward the chest. Then I rotated the 'freed-up' portion of the muscle to its new location. Next was the tedious job of suturing the good left half to the new improvised right half and then attaching the newly rotated portion to the muscle remnant on the rib cage. It's difficult to describe the awkwardness of this job. I was operating in a deep hole, holding the liver away from the suture needle, and avoiding the aorta and the large vein leading to the heart while placing the sutures. Alma synchronized Barney's respiration so I wouldn't puncture a lung with the suture needle. After about one and one-half hours, we completed the surgery. I removed the excess air from Barney's chest and closed the incision. Now, we would just have to wait and see if the improvisation would work.

I waited until Barney was awake to call Mrs. Galloway. I went over the procedure with her and told her of all the possible problems, but she was happy that everything up to this point had gone satisfactorily.

"Will Barney be coming home with me tonight? I'd love to have him with me, but I'm afraid I wouldn't know what to look for if he were to have some complication."

"No, he'll be going home with me. I'll want to watch him very closely. If all is going well, he'll be home by the weekend."

I was exhausted. The cow call at the Odum's the night before had deprived me of my normal amount of sleep and had started this day with less than my normal enthusiasm. That coupled with a surgery that had taken longer than I had anticipated and the unforeseen complications had depleted my usual reserve. But the surgery had gone well, and I was encouraged by its outcome. Now, if the sutures were strong enough to hold the makeshift diaphragm to the real diaphragm and if the blood supply was satisfactory, Barney should do well. One thing was certain: Barney would be on my mind for the next several weeks.

CHAPTER THIRTEEN

I was just getting situated in the truck after a late lunch and had barely pulled from the restaurant parking lot when my pager beeped. The number on the display was not familiar to me but the beeper was for emergency calls only so I pulled over at the first pay phone I saw and called.

"Hello, this is Dr. Brooks. Did you have an emergency?"

"Yes, Doc. This is Milford Hogsed in Blantyre and I've got a cow I believe you best take a look at. She's had the scours for a week now and none of my remedies has done good for her."

"Sure, Mr. Hogsed. I can take a look at her, and I've got some time now. Where are you located?"

"Great, Doc. Just take 64 past Rosman and then..." Mr. Hogsed finished with the directions and I was on my way. The drive took about thirty minutes and provided me with an unexpected surprise. Once I had turned off the main road and made two other turns onto gravel roads, I was confronted with a beautiful eight-foot waterfall. Not huge by the standards of many of the water falls in the county, but nevertheless, elegant in its own right. The flow of the falls was full thanks to the recent rains and the view was framed perfectly by a heavy growth of rhododendrons. The stream continued to parallel the road until I made my final turn into the Hogsed farm. Mr. Hogsed saw me coming and flagged me toward the barn.

"Sure appreciate your coming up here so promptly, Doc," said Mr. Hogsed as he talked around the long stemmed corncob pipe gripped tightly between his teeth.

"I'm glad I had the gap in my schedule, especially so after seeing the entry into your place and that beautiful waterfall."

"Yep, we're blessed here. God has seen fit to provide us with a nice place and even gave it some special touches like that waterfall. Sometimes when I don't have something to do and sometimes when I got something to do, I just like to go over there and sit. Kinda' does a fellow some good to hear the water hit the rocks below. Soothing, you know."

"What seems to be the matter with your cow? You mentioned something about her having diarrhea for the past week."

"She's right over there...next to the water trough."

As we walked toward the cow, I could see evidence of diarrhea in various areas of the lot. The fenced area was quite small, measuring probably no more than a hundred feet square. Hay had been thrown on the ground and had been trampled into the mud. There didn't appear to be any noticeable concern over hygiene. The cow, an Angus cross, was in poor condition and was at least one hundred fifty pounds underweight.

"Do you have another lot where you rotate your cow?"

"No, this is it. We're just raising her out for beef. Didn't figure I needed much space to do that." Mr. Hogsed pulled a tobacco pouch from the lapel pocket of his overalls and repacked his pipe. A few quick puffs and he was back in business. The aroma from the pipe was so sweet that it permeated and over-powered the odor from the cow's diarrhea.

"You're right. You don't need much space for that. Let me take a quick look at her." The exam didn't discover anything that was not already obvious. It appeared the problem rested around the confined quarters and a probable diet and parasite problem. These matters could be addressed without too much trouble. "Let's go to the truck. We'll discuss some steps you can take to increase her weight and correct that diarrhea."

We went over a few measures that Mr. Hogsed could take to improve his cow's condition, and I was about to leave when I noticed a full-size turkey running toward us. The bird slowed to a walk and then nuzzled his head directly under Mr. Hogsed's hand. Unconsciously, the man reached down and stroked the bird's head and then tickled the wattles under the bird's chin. The bird looked at him with the affection of a hound dog and moved even closer to him and placed one of his feet on the top of Mr. Hogsed's boot.

"That's quite a turkey. He's due for a shock come this time next week, I guess," I said thinking ahead to Thanksgiving.

"Oh, no. Not Tom. He's been with us a good while. He's got his own little loft over the barn. We sorta' got attached to him when we picked him up at the flea market 'bout three years ago. The wife fed him and fussed over him like you wouldn't believe. Ever since, he's been a pet. In fact, he gets first pickings from the supper leftovers -- even before the dog. The dog doesn't care for that too much but I guess he's come to realize that Tom really don't eat too much."

I left the farm with a new sense of what pet companionship could be. The thought of a turkey bonding to a person had never crossed my mind.

There wasn't much time left in the afternoon and no late appointments so I decided to go into town and get a haircut. It was close to quitting time, but as I turned onto West Main Street, I could see the shop was still open because the barber pole was turning.

"Come on in, Doc. I've been waiting for you all day," Ricky said as soon as I stepped into the shop.

"Waiting for me. How's that?"

"You'll be my last cut of the day. That's someone worth waiting for."

"I knew I was cutting it close but I saw the pole still turning. What's the origin of that pole anyway? The red, white and blue...is that just patriotic?"

"Just have a seat and I'll tell you what they taught us in barber school." Ricky dusted off the seat and motioned me to sit down. As he pulled the sheet over my clothes, he continued his explanation. "Sometime, in the seventeenth century, I think, doctors were forbidden by the church to perform surgery. They thought the human body was sacred and that men of God shouldn't touch the 'shameful parts.' Now, as I understand it, most medical schools at that time were located in universities controlled by the church and most doctors were also men of the cloth. The doctors decided that since the barbers already possessed razors it was only natural that..." Ricky was interrupted by Dwayne, who came in the shop followed closely by another man I didn't recognize.

"Don't mind us any, Ricky. I'm just trying to explain something to Gus, and it's taking more time than I expected. You don't mind, do you, if we just take a seat here while I complete my explaining?" Dwayne didn't wait for a reply but just sat down.

"Now, as I was saying," Ricky continued, "the doctors wanted the barbers to do all the blood-letting. Later, the doctors decided to put some distance between themselves and the barber. Believe it or not, the surgeons and the barbers were members of the same trade guild. So..."

"Gosh, darn, Dwayne, you sure must be pulling my leg if you expect me to believe that." Gus interrupted Ricky with his loud exclamation and hand waving as he motioned us to listen to Dwayne. "You fellows gotta' hear this. I was telling Dwayne about those confounded dogs that come into my yard and leave their deposits, I reckon is a nice way to put it, all over my yard. He said he never has that problem."

"I don't," Dwayne said as he shifted his head toward us. "It's a little trick my father taught me."

"I should have known," Gus said, "He was a regular plethora of worldly knowledge."

"A what?" Dwayne said with a puzzled look on his face.

"Never mind. What's the trick? And don't tell me you go to the neighbors and request that they restrain their free roaming dogs."

"Nope, don't want to waste my time. Here's all there is to it. About every two months, I go to the fish market and buy the old fish that no one else wants. The butcher gives me a really good price. Usually, I can buy it for…"

Ricky interrupted, "Wait a minute. You pay perfectly good money for fish that's decomposing?"

"Well, you might say it's on the edge of smelling. Anyway, I buy about four pounds of it. Before I unwrap it, I put on some throw-away gloves because the fish smells something awful, and then I take it to the four corners of my lot and deposit about a pound at each spot."

"That's the part I just don't get," Gus said. "The fish smell might keep them away if you had a small lot, but you've got four acres."

"That's what I was trying to explain to you when we came in the shop. It's not suppose to repel them, it's suppose to draw them in. You see, dogs love to roll in dead fish. I don't know why – they just do. After they roll in the fish, they eventually go home. By the time they get home, the dead fish has dried on their coats and there is nothing on this good earth that will really remove the stench."

Gus was in totally disbelief. "You're kidding."

"Oh no. When they get home, they lie down on the porch where they stink things up sufficiently to disturb the owners, and if they get into the house before the owner is wise – well, that's icing on the cake." The look on Dwayne's face revealed he was telling the truth. He wasn't bragging. He was just relaying his method. "After about four baths in tomato juice and vinegar, the dogs become almost tolerable again. The owners don't know what happened, but they do know they don't want it to happen again, so they keep their dogs up for a while."

I interjected, "Don't the dog owners get wise to what's going on?"

"Can't say for sure," Dwayne replied

Ricky was intrigued. "Haven't they found the fish piles?"

"Nope. I camouflage the fish by placing them in the wild flowers I've planted at each corner of my property. The fish finish their decomposition and become fertilizer. No one's the wiser, my yard is free of dog mess, and except for about two days every two months, it smells better because of the wild flowers."

Gus was becoming a believer. "Why do you do this every two months?"

"It's the darndest thing. I reckon people just plain forget and begin to let their dogs roam again. I've just learned that about every two months keeps things under control."

"Well," Gus said, "I would think that decomposing fish would smell for more than two days."

"It would if it wasn't for the cats."

"Cats?"

'Yep. The fish draws them, too, but they don't roll in it. They eat it and clean up the mess. And while they are there, they take care of field mice and moles. I haven't seen a rodent on my property in years. You know, I never thought of this before, but what do you suppose the butcher would do with all the old fish if I didn't buy it?"

"You're there every two months, right?" Gus said.

"Right."

"Then I suspect the thought never crossed his mind. Look, Dwayne, I want to get some more details. Let me buy you a cup of coffee," Gus said. And with that the two men left.

"Well, Doc, do you believe that?"

"I guess it plausible. I can just see the dog owner sitting in his favorite chair after a hard day at the office when his faithful dog comes to him and rubs against his legs waiting for that pat on the head. He reaches down to welcome the dog and before his senses detect it, he, his clothes and his house are engulfed in the odor of dead fish. Really, how could you make up a story like that? Just as I finished saying that, my eyes caught a sign that had been in the shop for ages but now seemed to take on more relevance.

HEADQUARTERS OF HUNTERS, FISHERMEN, GOLFERS, AND ALL OTHER LIARS

Go on with your history lesson on the barber pole."

"I don't remember where I left off. Oh yeah, okay, so the surgeons bartered with the barbers and told them they could have the symbol of the guild which was the red and white pole. The red represented blood and the white represented the rags used to wipe the wounds."

"What about the blue stripe?"

"Some say that represents veins and the red represents arteries. But, I probably told you more than I really remembered in the first place." Ricky turned the chair around facing the mirror. "How's that?"

"It's a little shorter than I wanted, but that's okay."

"Yeah, I saw that too. I got a little caught up in that story of Dwayne's and lost my concentration. But that's okay. It will grow back." And with that, Ricky went to the switch and turned off the barber pole.

I paid Ricky and he held the door open for me as I left. "You came in for a haircut and left with an education…the legend of the barber pole and Dwayne's solution for roaming dogs."

"Say, Ricky. Has Dwayne ever shown you his watch?"

"No, what's special about it?"

"Oh, nothing really. Next time he's in here, just ask him what time it is."

I went back to the office to pick up Barney and was met by a couple waiting at the front door.

The lady, in her mid-thirties and heavily bundled in a goose down parka, came towards me just as I opened the truck door. "I know you are closed but I was hoping you would be coming back. My boyfriend's cat is acting awful peculiar and we thought he should be seen before tomorrow morning."

"What seems to be the matter?" I asked.

"Well…he's just not himself. He's racing through the house, climbing the curtains, jumping on the counter tops, looking first one way and then the other, and then just going crazy."

"Let's take a look at him." I opened the front door and we went to the exam room. The cat was making some awful noises. The meow had that loud, deep groan that I usually associated only with Siamese cats. He was like a caged animal in the zoo with his head going side to side as he peered through the wire door of his carrier. His eyes had a crazy look about them. The man didn't look much better. He had a two-day beard stubble and a funny smell about him. As I tried to figure out how I was going to examine his cat, he just stood there; really leaning against the wall is more accurate, and said nothing.

Then all of a sudden, he said, "Where's the toilet?"

I didn't hear him at first because of the cat's howling. "What's that?"

"Where's the toilet?"

"It's behind the reception desk." I pointed the way and watched as he staggered toward the rest room.

As soon as he left, his girlfriend came very close to my face and whispered, "I'm not a doctor or anything, but I bet his cat ate some of my son's medicine. He's on an amphetamine for a condition he has and I found a pill on the floor right as we were leaving to come here."

"Well, that would explain that anxious behavior."

"Oh, and another thing," the young lady said as she got even closer and spoke in even a softer whisper, "my boyfriend smoked some marijuana on the way down here to calm his nerves about his cat. That's the reason I was driving. Don't tell him about my son's medicine. He can get pretty radical."

That explained both behaviors: the cat's hyped up on amphetamines and the man's high on marijuana. What a combination. The lady was about to give me more information when the man reentered the room.

"What's going on in here?" he slurred.

"Oh, nothing. We were just about to get the cat from the carrier," I said.

"It shouldn't take the two of you to…to do that. Let me have a hand at it."

"I wouldn't do that if I were you. The cat's acting wild and might get loose."

The man staggered to the table, and in a manner quicker than I thought capable, unlatched the door. The cat lunged from the carrier, climbed up the man's chest and leaped with abandonment at the exam room door where his claws stuck in the veneer. There he was hanging splay-legged on the door. We stood there in disbelief as we looked at this cat adhered to a vertical surface. The cat was fearful but unmoving. I grabbed the carrier from the exam table and gently worked it under him as he freed his nails from the door. He fell into the carrier and I quickly latched it.

"There, that should do it," I said. "You folks go on home. I'll keep the cat tonight and give him a sedative. He should be fine in the morning."

"Well, that's good, Doc," the man said, "but what…what do you supposed caused this? I don't want to go through this again."

"Hard to say. Catnip, maybe."

"Catnip? That would have to be some awesome kind of catnip."

"Call me in the morning. He'll be fine."

As the couple left, the woman turned back toward me and whispered a "Thank you."

The cat was exhausted from its escapade and was quiet with its rump resting against the cage door. I drew up a sedative and injected him in the leg. Within ten minutes he was resting quietly and I transferred him to a kennel cage. "He'll sleep that off and be a new cat in the morning," I thought. I wasn't equally positive about the owner.

Barney seemed curious about the activity, which was a good sign. I gathered him along with his IV fluids and put him in the truck. I was finished, both physically and mentally, for the day. All other emergencies would just have to wait. Tomorrow was another day.

CHAPTER FOURTEEN

The week passed quickly and before I knew it, Thanksgiving Day was upon us. Our family had much to be thankful for. As was our tradition for this day, we gathered at the table and then each of the boys, then Linda and I, told of at least one thing for which we were truly thankful. When we first started doing this, the boys were a little bashful about it but soon saw the value of expressing their appreciation to God for his provision.

Keith began the roundtable. "I'm thankful that I ran the Atlanta Peachtree Road Race this summer."

"Why is that, Keith?" Linda asked as she leaned forward in anticipation of his answer.

"Well, Dad promised Wyatt and me a digital watch if we ran a total of fifty miles before June. It's really a neat watch because it acts as a stopwatch, too. So that got me interested in running and timing how fast I could run a mile. Then Dad promised we could run the Peachtree if we trained really hard. It wasn't easy running in the heat of the day, but that's what we had to do if we were going to run on July fourth…plus, that's six point two miles. That training showed me what I could do if I really wanted to. And, although Dad won't admit it, both Wyatt and I beat him in that race."

"Now wait a minute, Keith. How can you be sure you and Wyatt finished before me?" I asked. "Where's your proof? There were twenty-five thousand people in that race and I never saw y'all until we gathered again at the closing ceremony."

"The finish times were sent in the mail. Our names were before yours."

"How come I never saw that list?"

"Because Mom hid it," Wyatt interjected.

"Oh," I said

"That's okay, Dad. You ran an awesome race for an old guy. Anyway, because of that race, the middle school coach is interested in training me for cross-country, and I think that would be fun. So that's why I'm thankful."

"How about you, Wyatt?" Linda asked.

101

"The pep club really paid me a compliment. They like the air brush work I've been doing before each football game and want me to continue with a larger version for the upcoming playoffs next Friday."

Linda added, "You really are a talented artist, Wyatt."

Travis was next. Being the youngest of the three boys, we didn't expect anything earth shaking. "I'm thankful that I can walk downtown by myself and not be snatched."

Linda had a surprised look on her face. "Not be snatched?"

"Yeah, you know, I'm safe in Brevard. I see all the stories on TV about kids being... what do you call it?"

"Kidnapped," I said.

"That's it. Kidnapped. I don't have to worry about that."

"We do live in a wonderful community, but that doesn't mean we can just drop our guard and be careless," I said.

Travis's face was just full of a young boy's enthusiasm. "But isn't it just great? I can go biking, play ball, go to the movie...you know, concentrate on the important things without that worry."

Linda continued. "It's my turn now, and I am just so thankful for my family, my friends and our church. I could go on and on but I'll do that after I get the rest of the dinner on the table. So, dear, what about you?"

"Where do I start? The list is almost too long, if that is possible. I guess I'm thankful for finishing the Peachtree even if I did come in third in the family," I said with a little sarcasm. "But, I have to say that I'm most thankful today for this family and the way that everyone pulled together over some tough years while I was establishing the veterinary practice. We moved to Brevard on a shoestring, a hope, and a vision of what life could be like in a small mountain community. I'm overjoyed about the way things have worked out." We concluded our roundtable of thanks with a prayer.

We had another tradition, which Linda had started just a few years earlier, and the boys were looking forward to it with much anticipation. It was the "black-eyed peas feast." Black-eyed peas are an important part of the Southern diet, yet we could not get the boys to eat them. That's when Linda came up with a brilliant idea. She collected a lot of silver coins and sterilized them in boiling water and then mixed them into the peas. It was just crazy enough to work. The boys were allowed to serve themselves and could keep the coins in exchange for eating the peas.

At first, the boys would dip the serving spoon into the bowl and wiggle it around until they thought they had hit pay dirt and then would pull out the money. They got quite adept at this. There would be a lot of coins and four or five peas. We were wise to their scheme so we established rules of engagement. They would get one pass through the bowl and would have to eat all the peas before they got another try. Sometimes, they came up empty and other times they came up wealthy. The idea was an instant success. It was like a conversion. They went from detesting the peas to loving them. There was also an unspoken rule that immediately following the dinner they all had to go outside to play, regardless of the weather.

While the boys were enjoying their feast, Linda placed the main dish on the table. It was a beautiful butterball turkey. The boys stopped their mining activities in the pea bowl long enough to let me know they wanted a thigh or a drumstick or just a slice. I served everyone except myself and was reaching for some cornbread when Linda asked, "Aren't you going to have some turkey?"

"Well, honey, I don't think so. Earlier this week I went to the Hogsed farm to take care of his cow and afterwards, while we were talking, this pet turkey of his came over to us and nestled up to us like a dog. Mr. Hogsed would reach down and pet him on his head and that bird would look up at him with those beady little eyes. There was some kind of communion going on between the two of them. Anyway, you and the boys see a nice butterball turkey on the table, and all I see is Tom. I've lost my appetite for turkey."

What Linda did next was a mystery because I surely didn't anticipate it and certainly can't explain it. Call it woman's intuition or whatever. Linda said, "I remember your telling me about that farm call and how that man had such compassion for his turkey, so…" she disappeared briefly from the table and then returned, "…I prepared a nice ham, too."

I was overwhelmed. The ham was hot and dressed with pineapple slices, cinnamon and some type of delicious glazing. Linda sliced a bite-size piece and fed it to me. What could I say? I made a quick mental inventory of my patients and could not think of one pig on the list. To this day, I have never tasted a better ham.

The relaxing Thanksgiving weekend ended abruptly at 9:00 a.m. Saturday morning with a phone call.

"Doc, this is Harold Axley and I know you hate to hear from folks on your day off and especially on Thanksgiving weekend, but I got a heck of a problem with my dog. I hate to admit it, but I fed him some left-over turkey, and he seems to be hurting a bit."

"Is he vomiting or having diarrhea…any other symptoms?"

103

"No, just very uneasy. I did see him straining to do his business a little while ago."

"Okay, Harold, let's do this. I'll meet you at the clinic in about twenty minutes and we'll take a look at him."

"Thanks, Doc, I'll see you there."

I left for the office right away so I would have time to pull the record and review it before Harold arrived. Just as I pulled the file from the shelf, my beeper sounded. I was hoping the call would be something I could handle over the phone or something that could at least be postponed a bit until I could finish with Harold's pet.

"Doctor Brooks, this is Barry Price in Etowah. A friend of mine is helping me castrate a hog and the worst possible thing has happened...his innards are coming through the sack where his balls are supposed to be. Just a minute, Doc." Barry didn't make any effort to cover the phone's mouthpiece as he shouted to whomever it was that was helping him. **"I got the veterinarian on the phone now. Just hold on, I'll be down to help you in a minute...I know he's big, just hold on.** Sorry, Doc, we do have a bit of a problem here. We need you to come out right away. Do you remember where our place is?"

"Yes, I know where you live, but it will be a while before I can get there. I've got another emergency on the way to the clinic right now."

"How long is 'a while,' Doc.? This hog is big, mean and, to say the least, he's not taking too kindly to what we've done. It's taking every ounce of strength Larry and Willard have just to hold him down."

"Who's Willard?"

"He's the fellow who did the cutting."

"I'll get there as soon as I see the other emergency. In the meantime, turn the hog on his back. Otherwise, he may throw his intestines all over the place."

"That's going to be a tough order."

"Why's that?"

"He weighs over two-hundred fifty pounds."

"Do your best," was all I could say as encouragement. Larry and Barry were two very stocky guys weighing in themselves at about two hundred fifty pounds apiece. Their properties joined each other on the back fence line, and they had probably gone into a joint venture to raise out a hog for food. They would just have to cope with the situation until I could get there.

Just as I hung up the phone, Harold arrived with his dog, Butch. I never did understand how the name Butch was tagged to a toy poodle, but that was probably another story that I didn't have time to pursue right now.

Harold cradled the little dog in his arms and went straight to the exam room. "I tell you, Doc, I'm not the most popular fellow in the house right now. The wife is one very upset person. She told me not to give Butch any left-over turkey because of the bones, and I told her it wouldn't hurt a dog. After all, a wild dog would eat a bird if he were starving. So, while she wasn't looking, I slipped him a leg bone. My pride and pocketbook are going pay the price for this."

"Let's have a look at him."

"Oh, you asked me if he was having diarrhea. He's not, but right after I called you, he strained and passed a little blood." Harold wasn't a young man, perhaps in his early seventies, and the pressure of this episode was clearly showing in his face. Even on this cold November day, there was sweat on his brow and an anxious look on his wrinkled face. "He's not going to die is he?"

"Harold, I'm going to get you to help me here. I'll put Butch on the table, and I want you to distract him by rubbing his head and gently talking to him. While you're doing that, I'll do a rectal exam to see if he's trying to pass a bone." I put on a rubber glove, lubricated my finger with Vaseline, and performed a rectal exam. There was a small bone wedged an inch and one-half in the rectum.

"Harold, we might be in luck. I can feel a bone just a little way up inside his rectum. Before, I try to remove that, I'll take an x-ray to see if there are any other bones."

I had barely disposed of the glove when the pager went off again. The displayed number was that of Barry Price. "Harold, hold Butch for a minute while I return this emergency call." I went into my office to call. I tried to sound upbeat and optimistic when Barry picked up the phone. "Barry, this is Dr. Brooks. How are y'all doing with the hog?"

I could barely detect the response over the panting noise of a man that sounded near exhaustion. "We ain't holding up too well. Willard left, but he wasn't much help anyway with his bad back. He left us in a fine mess. It's just Larry and me...make that just Larry while I'm talking to you on the phone...holding the hog. I'm just outside the basement door. The wife hooked up a long extension cord and banished me to the outside. She said I smell something awful and for me not to set foot in the house without hosing down first.

"I'm looking out the window at the two of them now. **Hold on a blame minute, Larry, I'm trying to hear what the vet has to say.** Excuse me, Doc, didn't mean to yell in the phone like that. Larry has some kind of hold on him that he claims he learned in high school wrestling…a full nelson or something like that if you can imagine that on a hog. Anyway, the hog has consented to be held this way for a while. But, in a spell, he'll be struggling again and then it will take the two of us to hold him down. It's not a pretty site when that happens. How much longer before you get out here, Doc? We can't hold on much longer."

"I think I can finish with this other emergency in about twenty minutes. I was about to take an x-ray of him when you paged me."

"Come as quick as you can, Doc. I never realized how strong a hog could be. One side of this wrestling match is going to give out pretty soon. I sure hope it's the hog."

The x-ray showed the remainder of Butch's intestinal tract to be free of bones. I packed Butch's rectum full of Vaseline and gently worked the bone fragment loose. The bone had not perforated the rectum and the blood that Mr. Axley had seen was from a minor irritation to the lining of the intestine. I dispensed some antibiotics to be administered for a few days and warned Harold about the hazards of feeding turkey bones to dogs.

Twenty-five minutes later I was at Barry's place and the sight was as picturesque as a Norman Rockwell painting. Barry, Larry and the hog were entangled in a contorted mess that defies description. Even though the temperature was in the low thirties, they were all covered in sweat. It appeared that the three of them were in a deadlock. Larry was on his side with his arms and legs wrapped around the hog. Barry had one of the hog's ears in each hand to control the head and the tusks. Barry had been right when he had said, "it wasn't a pretty sight." I jumped from the truck and rushed to them with the anesthetic that I had drawn up.

"Barry, gradually remove your hand from the hog's ear as I slide my hand over yours." The ear vein was distended and bulging and would be easy to inject. I threaded the needle into the vein and slowly administered the sedative. The hog relaxed and the two men collapsed to either side of the hog.

"Now, let's see what we have here." I rolled the hog on his back and saw the hernia with a piece of small intestine protruding from the opening. The men had done a marvelous job of preventing a full-fledge catastrophe. "This won't be too difficult," I assured them.

Neither man acknowledged as they remained prostrate and exhausted on the ground. I gathered the needed supplies from the truck, cleaned the wound and then closed it.

"You boys better move before the anesthesia wears off."

With a slow and labored effort, Barry pushed himself up and then staggered slightly as he put both feet under him. Larry had managed to get only to his knees and had both arms hanging as limp appendages with no strength left in them. Both men were saturated with mud, manure, hog sweat, and slobber.

"You know," Larry said, "I don't remember this kind of problem when my father used to castrate hogs."

"Your father probably castrated the pigs before they were twenty pounds. There's not too much to it when they are that size."

"Come to think of it, you're right. We always did it when they were small. How long we got to wait before we can send him to the butcher?"

"It will probably take a month of so for the male hormone to eliminate from his body. Any sooner that that and, let's just put it this way, the hams aren't going to taste too good."

Larry was standing now and with a gasping voice he managed to speak. "You know, Doc, Willard didn't do us right on this hog. I think next time we have one of these big fellows, we'll give you first shot at it."

As I got back in the truck, I could see the two men wiping the mess from their hair and clothes. Even with a good scrub down, they weren't going to be too popular with their wives for the next several days. There just something about hog odor; hot water and strong soap don't wash it away. It only wears off, and that, only with time.

CHAPTER FIFTEEN

The four-day weekend had passed too quickly for me but had still been restful in spite of the two emergencies on Saturday. Today was supposed to be a light appointment schedule. Susan had always scheduled the Monday following Thanksgiving as a light day because there were usually a few emergencies that would occur over a long weekend that would occupy the morning schedule. However, this weekend had been the exception. I was just about to leave for the office when the phone rang.

"Good morning, Doctor Brooks. This is Susan. No need to put on your running shoes this morning. There are no appointments until after lunch. I thought I'd let you know so you could run any errands you might have before you come in."

"Thanks, Susan. I think I will do a couple things before I come in."

"Who was that?" Linda asked.

"Oh, that was Susan. She just wanted to let me know there are no appointments until after lunch. Actually, that works out pretty well. I need to run by the hardware store and pick up a few things for the office. And it's only eight, so if I hurry, I can get there before the crowd arrives and won't have to wait."

"Good idea. Oh, wait just a minute, honey. I was going there this morning, too. No sense in the both of us going. How about picking up a few things for me?" She pulled a list from her pocket book. "Let's see…a package of forty watt bulbs, six kitchen sponges, some coat hangers…the plastic type, not those cheap wire ones, a bottle of cleaning ammonia, a pair of pliers and a light weight hammer. There, that should do it," she said as she planted the list in my hand and gave me a kiss goodbye. "I'll call you later today."

It was just a short drive to the hardware store and as I was paying the cashier, I wondered to myself what project Linda had planned with the pliers and the lightweight hammer. There was a certain amount of nervousness that crept into my being whenever

Linda gathered tools. However, in this case, I later learned that Linda just needed the tools to repair one of the boy's toys.

As I turned onto West Main Street, I saw a group of men congregated about the bench in front of the barbershop. As I got a little closer, I could see it was Arnold McCall, Bill Larenby and CJ. They were obviously discussing something. Bill had his arm in a sling and Arnold was shaking his head back and forth as if in disbelief, and CJ's arms were going in all sorts of directions with wild gesticulations. Curiosity captured me. I had to stop.

"Good morning, fellows. What are y'all up to this fine morning?"

"Good morning, Doc," Arnold said as if speaking for the three of them. "We were just discussing what happened this weekend. CJ knows the details best. Go ahead, CJ, tell the Doc what happened."

CJ moved toward me a bit. "I didn't think they could do that on the weekend, especially on Sunday."

"What's that, Jay?"

"It's all about the accident…well, the accidents I had last month. You remember how high the water got down on Wilson Road last month when the river went over its banks?" Jay had this gaze in his eyes and cocked his head upward as he continued. "I was going to the post office, didn't have any idea that the road was flooded, when all of a sudden I rounded a curve and there it was right in front of me!"

"What, Jay?"

"The high water, of course. That is what we are talking about, you know."

"Right, Jay. Well, go on."

"I wouldn't even have seen the water had it not been for the crow right in the middle of the road that was feeding on something or other. The sound of the screaming brakes must have scared him real bad. He popped up in the air and flew straight toward the truck, went through the windshield and hit me real hard right here in the chest. Hurt pretty bad, you know."

"I can imagine. But how did the bird get through shatter-proof glass?"

"There ain't no shatter-proof glass in a '51 Chevy truck."

"I didn't know you were into refinishing classics."

"I'm not. It's just an ordinary '51 Chevy truck that my paw gave me when I was sixteen. It's been a right good truck, reliable and all, so I just kept it."

"So, did you get the windshield replaced?"

"Yep, but it weren't any too easy to persuade the insurance company. Them windshields are hard to find. Then, would you believe it?"

"Believe what?"

"It happened again. About two weeks later, it was about ten o'clock at night. I was coming home from my bowling match, and a hoot owl makes a pass at me. But his timing was off a bit. He hit the windshield and went right through it again. Hit me in the same part of my chest and hit me so hard, it knocked the wind out of me."

"Gracious, Jay. What ever did you do?"

"I put the bird in one of those plastic shopping bags from Winn Dixie and took him straight to the taxidermist to see if he could stuff it for me. He told me it was too messed up to mount and not to bother him again so late at night."

"You went to a taxidermist at ten o'clock at night?"

"I needed proof for the insurance company; plus, I couldn't see wasting a perfectly good bird of that caliber. Well, anyway, the insurance woman looked at me real hard, Doc, and didn't really take too kindly to my story, especially since it had been only two weeks since the last windshield accident. I did some fast-talking and pulled up my shirt to show her the bird's beak marks. She had a funny kind of look on her face and pushed a check across the desk to me. So I got the window fixed, again."

"That's quite an experience, Jay."

"There's more"

"More?" I said incredulously.

"Yep. No sooner did I get the window replaced than I was going down Wilson Road again. This time, one of those fancy pet pigs – what do you call them?"

"Pot-bellied?"

"Yea, that's right. Well, he came out of nowhere. Now, who would have one of those, anyway? Ran right in front of me, and I hit him. He passed underneath the truck justa' bouncing from the oil pan to the rear axle. I jerked the truck on the shoulder of the road and jumped out to survey the damage to the truck. Front bumper messed up and a broken out head lamp."

"What about the pig?"

"He didn't look none too good, dead in fact, or so I thought. I knew the insurance lady would never believe this story so I thought... no need for this all to go as a loss. We'll just have bar-b-que this weekend. I went back to the cab of the truck and got my skinning

110

knife. Just as I was about to stab the hog to bleed him out, the sheriff's patrol car rounds the corner."

"Go on," I said like a kid watching criminal files on TV.

" Now, there I am, knife raised when he gets out of his car. He said 'What's going on here? Oh, it's you, Jay.' Thank goodness it was Jim Hargrove. We went to high school together. I told him what had happened. He could see the bruises on the hog and the damage to my truck, so it wasn't much of a hard sell to get him to believe me. Anyway, we talked about five minutes and I looked over at the hog, and he got up and just walked away – just like nothing happen. Beats anything I've ever seen."

"Is that the end of the story?"

"Of course it is. Don't you think that's enough? But, I'll tell you I learnt my lesson."

"What's that, Jay?"

"I ain't traveling no more on Wilson Road. There's other ways to get around this town, you know."

"Where's your truck now?"

"In the repair shop getting the windshield replaced."

"I thought you said it was your bumper and headlight."

"It was, but would you believe another bird went through the windshield?"

"That would be stretching things a bit."

"Funny, that's exactly what the insurance lady said when she canceled my insurance last night. On Sunday, would you believe? I asked her…"

"Confounded, Jay," Arnold said. "I didn't think you were going to go through that whole story again. We was a'talking about the steer."

"Wooley?" Jay said.

"Of course Wooley. That is the reason we are meeting here this morning. We need to plan our next step," Arnold said.

"Oh," CJ said.

Arnold continued. "Look, Doc, we've got ourselves a real problem. CJ said he told you about our first attempt to tranquilize the steer. That was a total disaster. Now, Bill here has bummed up his shoulder real bad in a second attempt."

"What happened, Bill?" I asked.

"I hit a tree a'chasing Wooley on my motorcycle. I was going over those rolls in the pasture just like those motor cross riders do in a race, and I guess I got caught up in the chase 'cause just when I was about to cut him off, he turned toward the woods. Must have been doing twenty miles per hour. Would you believe I hit a drainage culvert? Went right over the handlebars, I did, straight into an oak tree. Hurt pretty bad, but the doctor told me it was just a sprain. I tell you the truth, when we finally get this steer to the dinner table, I don't care if the steaks are good or not…I'm going to eat him out of spite."

"Look, fellows, I've got an open schedule this morning. Let's go see if we can round up this steer. See if you can get a few more men and let's meet at your place, Arnold, in say…thirty minutes?"

"Great!" Arnold said and he and the other two men jumped into their truck.

A short time later we reassembled at Arnold's place. He had rounded up six more men and had them in front of him and was briefing them on the peculiar nature of Wooley and why he had been so difficult to round up.

The men gathered around Arnold to listen to his briefing. It was almost like a military battle plan. He gave each man an assignment and told the overall strategy and then gave his conclusion about this particular steer they had named Wooley. "I tell you fellows, this is no ordinary steer. He's had the run of this pasture and knows every little rise and fall in the land. He's got some kind of sixth sense about him that sets him apart from other steers. He just knows when you're coming after him. He's not mean and he won't attack you, but don't get in his way 'cause he'll run right over you if you are between where he is and where he wants to go. Doc, you got anything you want to say before we get this thing started?"

"It seems CJ is the best archer here so I've given him some more tranquilizer for his arrow and positioned him just beyond that knoll." I pointed to a small hill next to an oak tree stump about fifty yards away. "What we need to do is just like Arnold said…let's put about fifteen yards between us and gently walk toward the steer. That will force the steer to walk away from us and right into the ambush. Just as he crosses the knoll, CJ will shoot his arrow. The tranquilizer will take about seven or eight minutes to take effect. So it's very important we don't rush the steer or he may panic and run."

"Where's CJ?" One of the men asked. "I don't see him out there."

"That tree stump is hollowed out. He's actually right down inside of it."

"Sorta' cramped up, isn't he? I mean that stump couldn't be more than three feet across," the man said.

"It is a bit tight but CJ can manage if we don't take too long getting there. Now, let's spread out and move toward that end of the pasture."

Arnold said, "Wooley's pretty doggone close to the pond. What if he decides to make a water escape?"

"If we don't rush him, he'll be okay," I said.

Just as the steer got close to the knoll, he raised his nose and sniffed. I realized what was happening. The steer passed on the downwind side of the tree stump and got a whiff of CJ and began to lope away from CJ and toward the pond. The men panicked. "Shoot him, CJ. Shoot him. He's headed toward the pond."

CJ stood from his concealed position, drew the bow and then with the aim of a skilled archer, planted the tip of the arrow in Wooley's left thigh. The steer was at a full gallop now and headed straight toward the pond.

"Oh, no," Arnold said. "He's goin' jump in the water."

All the men had broken ranks and were running with everything they had to catch up with the steer. CJ was in the lead. He wasn't a graceful runner with his hands and arms flying all over the place, but he was fast. The steer ran onto a small boating dock and lunged into the water. CJ was only yards behind him and without hesitation, dove into the freezing water. The rest of us, not being as brave as CJ watched from the edge of the pond.

Arnold was bent over from exhaustion and was resting with his hands on his knees. Through his heavy panting he managed to ask me with a labored breath, "What happens when the tranquilizer takes effect?"

"It won't knock him out, but it will affect his balance. We'll just have to hope he's a good swimmer."

CJ swam past the steer and was treading water as he waved his arms back and forth in front of the steer. Just as the steer turned toward the shore, he began to tilt starboard. CJ came beside him, slipped a halter over his muzzle and gently tugged him toward the shallow water.

"Well, I'll be!" said Arnold. "Never seen nothing like that before. I tell you, Doc, CJ has redeemed himself from all that confounded chatter we have to put up with."

CJ slogged through the mud at the edge of the pond and guided the steer onto dry ground. His lips, barely discernable under his drooping mustache, were thin and blue. He was shaking profusely and goose bumps were popping up all over his chest and arms. Bill pulled off his coat and wrapped it around CJ. While the other men tended to

Wooley, I quickly learned why the men sometimes referred to CJ as Cliché Jay. With a shivering voice, he still managed to say, "Man, that water is *colder than a bad girl's heart*, colder still than *an Alaskan well digger's butt*. I tell you that water is *cold enough to freeze the balls off a pool table.*"

"Well, Doc," Arnold said, "I guess we finally cornered the beast. We'll put him in the feeding pen for a couple months and pour the grain to him and get him ready for the dinner table. Say, CJ, I've never seen you move so fast. Where did that come from?"

"*No time to doodle*. It was time to *fish or cut bait.*"

"But, didn't it concern you that the water was probably only fifty degrees or so?"

"Well, I didn't want to *Monday-morning quarterback* this situation with whether or not I made the right decision. After all, *a bad decision is better than no decision at all.*"

"But you didn't hesitate. You dove right into that freezing water."

"*He who hesi...hesi...hesitates is lost,*" CJ chattered between gasping breaths.

"And the halter? Where did that come from in the middle of the pond?"

"It was all *in the scheme of things*. You know what they say, *Good results follow a good plan*. I had it strapped on my suspenders.*"

CJ walked behind the men and gathered his bow from the tree stump as Arnold and I followed.

"Tell me, Doc. Have you ever in your life seen a man that can talk so much and say so little?"

"He did save that animal's life and your investment with his quick action."

"You're right there, but you know that other thing I said about him after he pulled himself from that cold water."

"What's that?"

"You know...that he had redeemed himself from all that chatter we have to put up with."

"You did say that."

Arnold cocked his hat to the side of his head and with a grin said, "I'd like to retract that statement. No. On second thought, the boy did good." With that Arnold jogged forward and put his arm around CJ and said something that made the two of them laugh joyously.

CHAPTER SIXTEEN

Surgery has always been one of my favorite parts of veterinary medicine. It's different from the medical aspects. With surgery there are some immediate rewards: a fractured leg or a laceration repaired, tumors removed, a neutering procedure completed, and in some cases, a life saved. A complicated fracture is much akin to putting together a three dimensional puzzle. Generally, whatever the problem may have been is resolved once the surgery is completed. There is some instant gratification. That's not always so with medical cases. Diagnosing problems is a complete issue in itself. Blood work, medical imaging, EKGs, and a whole host of other procedures may be necessary to "work up" a case to arrive at an accurate diagnosis. But surgery does not always resolve the problem and bring the patient back to its former and unaltered self. Even though veterinary medicine has achieved great advances in recent years, some problems have only a salvage procedure solution. Ming Tow was such a case.

Mr. Trocker put Ming Tow on the exam table and said in a lackadaisical manner: "What can you do about this?"

Ming Tow was a Shih Tzu, a small flat-faced breed that is known for its good temperament and affectionate behavior. It is also one of the breeds that has very prominent and protruding eyes. The pug-like face means the protection that is usually afforded to the eyes in a longer nose breed is absent. The socket that houses the eye is also shallow. Consequently, what might have been a bumped nose in a collie or lab turns into a serious eye injury to a Shih Tzu. Ming Tow's left eye was hanging from the eye socket and dangling on his cheek.

"When did this happen, Mr. Trocker?" I could determine by the dry appearance of the eye that the injury was not within the last few hours.

"I noticed it yesterday at lunch, but I just didn't have the time to get over here. I had to get the oil changed in the truck. Besides, it didn't look this bad. The eye was just a little swollen and sticking out more than usual."

"There's no hope for the eye. The only thing I can do is remove the eye and close the socket."

115

"You mean to tell me you can't put it back in place? I don't want Ming Tow to be blind or have just one eye. Just put it back in place and I'll take my chances."

"No, I won't do that Mr. Trocker. When you noticed the eye yesterday, could you determine if Ming Tow was in pain?"

"Well, he did act a little out of sorts. He was rubbing his eye on the carpet and rolling over a lot. I gave him an aspirin to help him with the pain. It calmed him down some."

"If you had brought him in at that time, we might have had a chance to save the eye and his vision but we have lost that opportunity. When an eye pops out like that, there is a very short window of time for a successful repair. We are talking minutes, not hours. If I could put the eye back in the socket, we would be courting with disaster. Infection and glaucoma would rear their ugly heads and necessitate further and more complicated surgery. All we can do now is remove the damaged eye and close the eyelids."

"He's going to look funny with just one eye."

"Not really. Once the hair grows back in place, you will hardly notice there is anything missing. And fortunately, Ming Tow won't miss the eye too much. He'll get around just fine."

"All right, if you say so. Go ahead and fix him up and I'll pick him up a little later this afternoon."

I couldn't get over how unaffected Mr. Trocker was handling all this. It was almost as if there was no compassion at all for the animal's discomfort. "Ming Tow will be staying the night. We'll want to make sure he recovers properly from the surgery and that we have good pain management control before he goes home. Check with Susan up front. She'll give you a fee estimate for the procedure."

As soon as Mr. Trocker left, Alma began the preparations for surgery. She inserted an intravenous catheter and did the preliminary clipping of the hair around the eye. Next, we induced anesthesia, completed the clipping and surgical cleaning and moved Ming Tow to the surgery area. He was given one final cleaning and then draped for surgery. Once the drapes were in place, all I could see of Ming Tow was his pitiful injured eye.

The surgery was straightforward. I removed the damaged eye and most of the muscles within the socket and then prepared for the closure. To make the face look as normal as possible, I removed some of both the upper and lower eyelid margins so that when everything healed, there would not be a sunken appearance where the eye had once been. The new margins came together and were closed with suture material. I gave Ming Tow an antibiotic injection and pain medication and instructed Alma on the immediate aftercare. Ming Tow would do fine. He had been through some ordeal over the last twenty-four hours, but he was now well on his way for a good recovery.

It was six o'clock when Ming Tow recovered from the anesthesia and was sitting up in his cage. He looked comfortable and free of pain. Alma said she wanted to stay with him another hour or so before she left to go home just to make sure the little fellow would do well during the night.

"Thanks, Alma. You're an angel to stay around. I'll leave Ming Tow in your care and then see you tomorrow morning."

Darkness came with an abruptness that cold night in early December. The sparse light the stars may have cast on this moonless night was robbed of its brilliance by the heavy overcast of clouds. Rain or snow appeared imminent. As I left the office, I noticed the leaves on the rhododendron bush next to the building had already coiled into tight spirals to conserve the little warmth they had gathered during the day. Early settlers to this area used to determine the temperature by the tightness of the coil on the leaf. I had the convenience of a thermometer on the side of the building. It was twenty-six degrees. I checked the truck for supplies just in case a farm emergency would rear its unwanted head this evening. At least if I were called out, I wouldn't have to come to the office to pick up anything. I peered out the windshield as I turned the ignition key and was still amazed at the darkness. Except for the dash panel lights, there was not a ray of light anywhere. If the absence of light could be rated on a scale of zero to ten, this night would surely qualify as a nine. Later that evening I was reminded of another place where the darkness could not even escape itself.

My pager abruptly ended my trip home to a warm fire and hot dinner before I had even traveled to the exit of the parking lot. I went back into the office and called.

"Doc, this is Fred. I've got a two-month old calf out here that got her rear end coming out."

"Fred, I was just on the way home for dinner. What do you mean 'her rear end is coming out?' Will it wait?"

"Hellfire, Doc, it's her ass that's coming out. Now, if it were yours, would you ask a fool question like that?"

"I'll be right there, Fred."

Fred McCrary is one of my favorite clients and over the years had become a good friend. He is a native of Transylvania County and a man of few words. He knew an emergency when he saw one and was straight to the point to insure I understood exactly the nature of the problem. Fred's bond was his handshake and his word. "Right's right and wrong's wrong, and there're not many gray areas between," he would say. He was a man of many talents and had done well in various business ventures over the years. He had owned and operated a concrete plant, farmed cattle, and in the past several years had excavated sand from the French Broad and other rivers to satisfy commercial and government contracts. He had sold a large tract of land a few years ago and had paved a driveway for one of the new homeowners. I had heard a story once that the homeowner was derelict and didn't pay Fred for the work, so Fred "repossessed" the driveway. Fred's a tough man but fair, and if there were ever to be a time when sides would have to be chosen for something, I would want to be on Fred's side because that would be the worthy side. The drive to the farm was short and Fred was waiting for me at the pasture gate as I arrived.

"Thanks for coming, Doc. We'll just go through this gate here and over to that shed. The calf's in there." Fred was wearing a heavy wool coat and pullover hat with earmuffs. He pointed with his flashlight to a small secondary shed that he used to isolate sick calves. The darkness absorbed the thin beam of the light, but I could see enough to know that I didn't want to cross the area twice. It was four inches deep in mud and water from all the rains and it would be a little treacherous just to get the needed equipment there without falling.

"Just a minute, Fred. Let me slip on my coveralls and boots and make sure I got everything I need before we go over there." I slipped in the cab of the truck and pulled my coveralls over my clothes and then slipped on a pair of insulated black rubber boots. My large animal medical bag was well supplied so I grabbed it and we made the jaunt to the shed.

Fred slipped in the mud about halfway across the muddy terrain but managed to catch himself before falling. "I tell you the truth, all this rain we are getting and then it freezing and then getting more rain is causing me some problems. The river's so high, the field won't drain and my cows are having problems just getting to the feed trough."

We slouched our way to the shed and found the calf in the back corner where Fred had placed her. He had put a blanket around her earlier to keep her warm. After a quick appraisal of the calf, I could see there was a serious problem. The rectum was protruding out the

118

anus about six inches and had already lost its natural red color and was now black. Gangrene had already begun. "How long has she been this way?"

"Not sure. I think she was okay this morning, but I was in such a rush taking care of all the other problems this rain has caused, that I didn't check her real close until tonight. What would make that come out like that anyway?"

"In a calf this age we could have several things, but generally a prolapsed rectum follows straining to have a bowel movement or a problem with diarrhea."

"Well, she has had the scours for a couple days. Quite a bit of diarrhea, too, I'd say."

"We'll have to amputate this dead tissue."

Fred pulled off his earmuffs as if he hadn't clearly heard me. "You're going to cut off her ass? How's she going to do her business? That seems to me to be a pretty damn important part of her anatomy." Fred never was one to mix words. He said exactly what he meant and curse words were not meant as anything other than a strong adjective or adverb.

"It is important all right, but what we have here is a severe infection. If we don't remove the dead tissue, she will die. She may die even after we remove it because of the infection that is already in her body. The procedure to reconstruct the rectum is not difficult and should take about half an hour." But I could see we would have a bit of a problem with any semblance of a sterile procedure. Even at two months of age the calf was too heavy for the two of us to carry across the mud. We would have to do the best we could with what we had. Veterinarians, as a lot, are used to performing surgery under poor conditions. When large animals collapse in the field, there is little choice but to work on them at that point whether the problem requires a cesarean section or some other procedure.

"Fred, grab that bale of hay over there and set it next to the calf. We'll use that as an instrument table." I pulled two surgical towels from my medical bag and placed one between the straw on the ground and the prolapsed tissue. I wrapped the other towel under the rectum and gave the two ends to Fred who would support the rectum in this makeshift sling while I prepped the area for surgery. The calf had cooperated well up to this point, but I knew she wouldn't with the next part so I gave her a spinal block with a dose of lidocaine.

"Hold that flash light steady, Fred." A prolapsed rectum can be visualized as a tube sock that has been partially turned inside out and

119

the toe portion removed. One end would represent the end attached just inside the body. Now, if you reach into the sock and pull a portion of the sock toward you, you have the rough resemblance of the relationship of a prolapsed rectum. I would have to cut through four layers, remove the gangrenous part and then suture the good parts together. The tricky part is to keep one portion of the rectum from slipping back inside the calf once I had finished the complete cut through all four layers. I attached four tissue forceps evenly around the healthy rectal tissue to secure it and then began the incision. The amputation of the diseased portion took about five minutes. I spent a few more minutes controlling some minor bleeders and then poured lactated ringers over the area to keep the tissue moist. I was concentrating on the dissection intently and didn't notice the flickering of the flashlight. The bright light changed to a dim yellow and then, just as quickly, extinguished.

"Hellfire, Doc, the batteries are dead."

The darkness level that I had earlier given a "nine" had just gone to "ten." Imagine, we were in a totally dark shed surrounded on the outside by total darkness. There was no gradation of darkness. The darkness in front of my face was as dark as the farthest corner of the shed. It was pitch black dark. It was at that moment that I remembered something darker than this night. It's peculiar why we think of things when we do. Here I was at the crucial part of an amputation, and I was thinking of another place and time that was darker than this. Maybe my brain was grasping for something that would give me hope that I could complete this surgery. A few years back, I had visited France and on the trip had had the occasion to tour a fourteenth century fort. Deep under the fort was a dirt-floor dungeon. There, total darkness took on a whole new meaning. It was cold, damp, infested with rats and with the annoyance of their chatter, and without hope of escape. Prisoners would never see light except for the brief rays that might seep in when food was passed through a small slit at the base of the dungeon door. In that darkness I could not see my hand in front of my face. Fred interrupted my melancholy diversion.

"Hold what you've got, Doc. I think I've got a lantern next to the door."

I could hear Fred cautiously making his way across the shed. There was a dull thud and then "Damn."

"Are you okay?"

"Yea, I'm fine. Do you remember that low beam we dodged coming in here?"

120

"Let me guess. You found it."

"Right. That jolt made me swallow some tobacco juice. That wasn't too damn pleasant, but I did find the lantern."

"Great! Bring it over here."

Fred lit the lantern before making the return trip. The light cast some strong shadows but that was a mild inconvenience compared to total darkness. Actually, the lantern provided a good overall light to the whole area and enabled me to finish the suturing in about twenty minutes. I washed the area one last time and inverted the newly created rectum into its proper position. As I gathered my instruments, Fred attended to the comfort of the calf and insured the blanket was secured to keep the animal warm.

As we returned over the muddy area to the gate, we discussed the treatment Fred would give to the calf over the next several days. After discussing those details, I couldn't help myself. "Fred, I heard that you once repossessed a driveway from a person that didn't pay you for your work. Now, I don't doubt that you could do that, but tell me, how do you repossess a few tons of concrete?" By this time I had opened the front door of the truck and the cab light provided all the light I needed to see a smile come across Fred's face.

"It's simple. All it takes is a front-loading tractor and a few jackhammers to break up a driveway into small pieces. Of course, you need one or two dump trucks to haul it off."

"You mean to say that you just went onto the man's property and took away his driveway?"

"It wasn't his driveway. He never paid for it, so I just took it back."

"What did he do?"

"Nothing. He was out of town. He was set back a bit, though, when he got back from vacation and saw dirt where the driveway used to be. Of course, it had rained a lot that week so there was a lot of mud. He said he was a lawyer and that he was going to sue me."

"Gracious, Fred."

"Ah, I wasn't worried. He knew he was wrong and that I was right. All I had done was call his bluff when he refused to pay me. You know, I bet you he's not much of a poker player. Otherwise, he would have known never to bluff me unless he was holding a winning hand."

"Did you ever hear from him again?"

"No. I see him from time to time downtown, but he generally crosses the street when he seems me coming. Well, Doc, you better get on home. I suspect your dinner's waiting."

"Right, I am hungry. Keep me posted on the calf's condition." With that I jumped in the truck and left. Somehow the night seemed brighter on the way home.

CHAPTER SEVENTEEN

The next morning started with a relaxed schedule that was typical for December. Christmas shopping, traveling and the general festive spirit this time of year eased the workload in a veterinary practice. Pet owners tend to put off routine vaccines and exams until the Christmas holidays are over. The emergencies, which are never planned, of course, are still there and sometimes seem to stack on top of each other. Today would prove to be an example of that.

The McHenry's brought in Lexus, their Himalayan cat, for vaccines and a routine examination. The elderly couple was the first appointment of the morning and possibly the only one until after lunch. But after a late and cold last night, I was content with a slow morning.

"Lexus is the perfect image of health and he's lost two pounds over the last six months. You've done an excellent job in getting him to his optimum weight."

"It hasn't been easy, I can tell you that," Mrs. McHenry said. This little guy can become beastly when he doesn't get all he wants to eat. I wonder, Doctor, if I could comment on something my husband and I saw last Tuesday? I don't want to put you behind schedule for this morning though." Mrs. McHenry peered out the exam room door toward the reception area to see if anyone would be able to hear what she was about to relate.

"Go right ahead. I've got plenty of time this morning and no one is waiting."

"Well…let me just tell you what my husband and I saw last week at South Broad Field. We were driving toward town looking for the driver's license office. We didn't know exactly where it was when we saw a man walking something on a leash in the tall grass next to the sidewalk. It was some of that tall grass that survived the freeze so we couldn't see exactly what kind of pet he was walking. We assumed it was a Yorkshire Terrier or a Chihuahua or something small like that. My husband said hello to the man and before he asked for directions, he jokingly asked the man what kind of 'monster' he had on the end of the leash." The wrinkles on Mrs. McHenry's face straightened out and almost disappeared as she came to the next part.

"Now, I don't know who this man is, but he has sort of crimson hair and a very strong chin line. Anyway, he stopped and with a sinister smile on his lips he said, 'Now most folks take their dog for a walk, but I take my snake for a crawl.' Almost simultaneously he pulled back on the leash and there, right in front of us, was the largest snake I've ever seen in my life. It must have been ten feet long."

"More like twelve feet, if you ask me," Mr. McHenry said.

"My heart went straight to my throat, and I passed out. It was a horrible experience. Honey, you tell the doctor the rest 'cause I don't remember anymore."

"Not much more to tell. I saw this huge ten or twelve-foot snake pop its head up and look straight at me. Then I saw Mildred, here, fainted dead away with her mouth wide open. I just floored the gas petal and headed straight for the county hospital to get treatment for my poor wife. But the screaming tires woke her up so we just went for coffee instead to settle our nerves."

I knew straight away that the man was Jack Williams. He had a twelve-foot Boa Constrictor snake that he kept in the back of his shoe shop and often took it to the ball field at South Broad to give it exercise. Just the thought of Jack and that snake made me smile inside. I hated that my inward amusement and humor were at this couple's expense but they seemed to have overcome the shock and were now able to talk about the incident without too much anxiety. "My goodness, what an experience! Are you folks okay?"

"Oh, we are fine now and none the worse for the wear. You know we are fairly new to this community, but it would seem to us that you have a few unique people living here."

Not realizing it, the McHenry's had set a positive tone to my day with their story. After the couple left, I sat at my desk in the hopes of reducing the large administrative workload that had gone unattended this past week. But that wasn't to be.

Just as I was starting on the accounting report, Alma told me the Olivers had arrived with their Labrador Retriever, Last Chance. The dog had received his name about ten years ago when the Olivers had rescued him from his inevitable fate at the local animal shelter. Last Chance had collapsed the previous evening and had been rushed to the emergency clinic in Asheville. There, the clinicians had stabilized him and had run some tests. They had taken a radiograph that revealed the presence of a mass in the abdomen. The next morning he was transferred to us for further treatment.

The Olivers looked worn out. They had been up most of the night and their mutual exhaustion was unveiled in their faces. They needed rest so I told them to go home and that I would call them once we had determined a course of treatment.

The blood report from the emergency hospital showed a dramatic drop in Last Chance's red blood cell count and a drop in his blood protein levels. These findings in conjunction with the location of the mass on the radiograph were strongly suggestive of a tumor on the spleen. ...a tumor that had ruptured and then sealed itself temporarily from further bleeding. We performed an ultrasound because I didn't want any surprises and wanted to be sure of what I would encounter at surgery. The ultrasound confirmed the mass was on the spleen. Next, we repeated the blood count and found that it had improved from the previous evening. This was encouraging because it meant there was no active bleeding, and that we would be able to do the surgery without administering blood. But just as a safety precaution, Alma went home and picked up her dog, Winston, to act as an emergency blood donor should the occasion call for supportive blood.

I called the Olivers and explained the necessity for removing the spleen. They had some understandable concerns about the surgery and possible complications of Last Chance not doing well without a spleen. I explained to them that the spleen functioned as a filtering organ and was involved in the body's immune system but that a dog could function without infirmity without a spleen. They gave me consent to perform the surgery.

After we had started intravenous fluids and reached a good anesthetic level, I made a ten-inch incision in the dog's abdomen. The incision was intentionally large to allow the handling of the mass without risk of rupture while lifting it from its location deep in the abdominal cavity. As soon as I opened the incision, a belly full of blood met me. This was not fresh bleeding but blood from the rupture the previous evening. Alma opened a sterile pack that contained a suction probe and rubber tubing and turned on the suction pump. All the blood would have to be removed before I could see the tumor. Sometimes, in cases of abdominal bleeding the blood can be salvaged and administered to the patient, but in this case, we did not do that since the source of the blood was from a tumor that was probably cancerous.

With the blood removed, I could now see the tumor. It was a very ugly, irregular shaped purple mass attached to the end of the spleen. I gently elevated it from the abdomen and began dissecting away adhesions. The spleen has a lot of blood vessels leading to and from it and each had to be clamped with metal clips. This is a tedious job but not particularly difficult, and once this was completed, I severed all the vessels and removed the spleen and the tumor.

Alma had done a wonderful job with the anesthesia throughout the surgery and began to decrease the dose as I closed the incision. She gave him pain medication through the intravenous catheter and continued her evaluation of his vital signs. About fifteen minutes later we moved Last Chance to the recovery area where Alma stayed with him until he was able to hold up his head. I called the Olivers and gave them a promising report.

Remember what I said about how emergencies tend to stack up? No sooner had we returned the surgery area back to some semblance of order than Mr. Powell rushed through the front door carrying his Siamese cat that had been shot through the chest.

A year ago Sinbad had been shot in his left rear leg by a small caliber rifle shell. He was lucky though. The bullet that time was of the steel-jacket, high velocity variety. A bullet of that type generally passes through its target with such speed that little vibration is created. That means that a lot of collateral damage is avoided by the break-up of the projectile and the so-called "tumbling" effect. The bullet did hit the large bone beneath the knee, the tibia, but the fracture was clean and easily repaired with a stainless steel bone pin.

Mr. Powell put Sinbad on the exam table. "Darndest thing I've ever seen. He's clearly been shot…you can see the bullet hole right there in the chest…" Mr. Powell pointed to a hole in the left side of the chest…"but Sinbad doesn't seem to be hurting any. He's a little bit more quiet than usual, but that's about all."

Mr. Powell had sworn after last year's episode that Sinbad could join, as he put it, "his worthless kin" in cat heaven if he ever got himself shot again. He said the cat was a snake disguised as a cat, that it bit him, scratched him and except for one thing was no better than a rubbish pile. "He's the ultimate rodenticide. If there were another hundred like him, Terminex could just pack up and leave town. Moles and field mice don't even run from him. They just take one look and die of a heart attack." That was after the last bullet wound. Sinbad had really got himself in a fix this time…a bullet wound to the chest without an exit hole. The bullet could be anywhere and probably had done considerable damage. I was sure I was looking at a dead cat that just hadn't realized its fate. It looked like we would have to revisit the whole "worth" issue all over again. I was preparing to tell Mr. Powell the extent of tests we would have to do and then what the treatments might entail when he spoke.

"I guess you ought to fix him up. He's not worth five rolls of pennies, but he's mine and I best take care of him."

"He is an amazing cat, but this wound may be misleading."

"How's that?"

"There's an entry hole, but I don't see where the bullet came out. That means it was either a spent bullet that hit him and didn't go deep into the chest or the bullet lodged itself somewhere deeper inside Sinbad's body. I'll need to take some x-rays to find the bullet."

We took two pictures of our little patient. We laid him on his right side to take the first picture and then took a second one with him on his back. These two pictures taken at right angles to each other would allow a three dimensional interpretation of the bullet's location inside the body. Sinbad was uncharacteristically cooperative and allowed us to take the radiographs without any sedation. Alma put the pictures through the processor and then posted the films on the view box.

"Amazing," I thought as I studied the bullet's path. The bullet entered between the fourth and fifth rib on the left side of the chest and passed behind the heart. Here the bullet should have hit the aorta, esophagus or the main vein coming to the heart. It missed them all and proceeded through the diaphragm, liver and then impaled itself in the right kidney where it came to an abrupt halt and imparted most of its damage.

"Mr. Powell, you've got one lucky cat. It looks like he might lose a kidney from his injuries, but right now that may be the extent of it. We won't know for sure until we get in there surgically to see if there are any other concerns."

"What about the chest wound?"

"The bullet is a small caliber, probably a .22, and entered at a sharp angle and incredibly missed all the vital structures in the chest. The muscle covering the chest wall and the skin slid back over the wound and sealed it, so we are okay there."

"That cat's something else. I reckon the rodents are going to get a brief vacation from their tormentor. Will he be able to do his soldiering, that's what we call it, when he gets well?"

127

"He'll need to recover from his injuries first, but I suppose he'll be back to his ornery self in a few weeks."

Mr. Powell gave a simple smile, shook his head in an affirmative manner and left.

While I had been talking to Mr. Powell, Alma had already prepared Sinbad for surgery and installed an intravenous catheter. I gave Sinbad a preanesthetic drug and then placed a tube in his trachea to administer the gaseous anesthetic. Alma finished the preparations and did the surgical scrub while I scrubbed up and put on my surgical gown.

By the time I returned to the surgery area, Alma had everything ready and had connected Sinbad to the pulseoximeter which would monitor his heart rate, body temperature and blood oxygen content. "Great, Alma. I guess we are ready to start."

The radiograph had provided us with a good picture of what I was to find once I made the incision into the abdomen. There were no surprises. The bullet penetrated the liver causing it to have a slow bleeder, which would require attention but that could wait for now. I needed to repair the hole in the diaphragm first to insure there would be no problems with Sinbad's ability to breathe. I separated the liver and diaphragm from each other by packing a few gauze sponges between them. That would give me enough space to work and to maneuver the suture forceps. The hole was small and easy to reach. I closed it with one suture. The major damage was limited to the right kidney. The kidney had been severely damaged and had lost most of its anatomical structure in absorbing the impact momentum of the bullet. The bleeding was minimal so there wasn't much visual interference in finding the blood vessels to the kidney and clamping them. Next, I tied off the small tube, the ureter, that carries the urine from the kidney to the bladder. I lifted the kidney out and deposited it into a surgical bowl. Once the kidney was out, I turned my attention to the liver which had a seeping wound that was bleeding minimally. I was able to control the hemorrhage with just digital pressure. I finished the abdominal closure as Alma gave an injection for pain.

I was reasonably confident that Sinbad would do fine with only one kidney. The body can function without any handicap on one kidney if it is normal. Ideally, more extensive testing is done on the proposed remaining kidney before removing a kidney when time permits. In Sinbad's case, we had neither the time nor the equipment to do such testing. However, the kidney tests we had done last year when he was shot the first time were normal. Now, if we could keep him from being shot a third time, he should do just fine.

I sat down and called Mr. Powell. "Sinbad did wonderfully through the surgery, but we did have to remove his right kidney. He can manage perfectly well with just one kidney and should be back in action in short order."

"He may be put into retirement. I think I've found out who's been shooting him. Can't know for sure, but I believe it's the man just around the curve from me. I stopped by the hardware store on the way home from your office and saw him buying some dry corn. He told the clerk that he had finally nailed the 'blasted demon cat' that had killed two of his flying squirrels. You know, to Sinbad, a rodent's a rodent. It doesn't make any difference that it can fly."

So there we were. Only half the day gone and we had already completed two major emergency surgeries with very favorable outcomes. I felt blessed with my staff. They made my work easy and enjoyable. Susan had taken over where I had left off with both the Olivers and the Powells and lifted their spirits. She had reassured them about the need for the surgery and that their pets would do well through the procedure. She had called both the clients again after I had talked to them just to update them on their pets' recovery progress. She had truly eased their concerns. Alma was my right hand in surgery. She monitored and adjusted the anesthesia with the skill of an anesthesiologist. And she anticipated my needs during surgery. If I needed suture material, she had it ready before I would ask. She relieved me of many decisions which enabled me to concentrate my full efforts on surgery. After surgery Alma was wonderful in recovery. She had a gift for picking up the minutest change in the patient. No patient under her care would ever want for anything. Warm blankets to cover them and comfort towels under them were just two of the standard things she did to ease their return into the conscious realm.

By the time Susan, Alma and I had cleaned the surgery room after Sinbad's surgery, Last Chance was struggling to stand in his kennel run. We all stopped what we were doing and watched. He stretched his front two legs well in front of him and then cautiously pulled his rear legs under his body. He wobbled from side to side at first but then became steady. Labs are wonderful dogs. They have an abundance of the love emotion and that is exactly what Last Chance demonstrated. Even after all the hardship and pain he had endured during the last twenty-four hours, he was blissfully wagging his tail and eager to please any humans that might be in the area. He turned his head slowly toward Alma and me. His big brown eyes and gentle face were the prize for the day. What more reward could a veterinary team want? Well, it would be nice if Sinbad would wake up purring or at least be more congenial than his usual self. But why ruin a good morning by hoping for the impossible.

CHAPTER EIGHTEEN

November and December had been busy months. And they had been strenuous months as well. The appointment schedule had remained about the same as in previous years, but the emergency workload had been heavy and, at sometimes, almost more than my physical stamina could endure. But I couldn't complain. I had a real sense of enjoyment and accomplishment in my work and the variety of cases kept my interest level high. This morning had been especially rewarding. I saw both Last Chance and Sinbad for their surgical follow-up and to remove their sutures.

Last Chance was wagging his tail with so much vigor that I had difficulty removing the sutures. I teased Mr. Oliver, "Last Chance is just a typical old Labrador. All he wants to do is please the humans around him. Alma, keep fueling him with those biscuits so I have at least an even chance of removing these sutures." Last Chance would gobble the treat, and in that brief moment, I would be able to snip one more suture. Finally, all the sutures were removed. The Lab nuzzled Alma one more time for that final biscuit. "I can see the surgery didn't damper his appetite." I said to Mr. Oliver.

"Damper? Why just the opposite is what I'd say. The way I figure it, the tumor was taking up space in his belly and once it was gone, he had more room for food," Mr. Oliver said with a broad smile on his face.

"He looks great, Mr. Oliver. You've done a good job nursing him back to his old self. Keep pushing the groceries to him until he gains his weight back, but don't overfeed him this winter." With that we lifted Last Chance from the table and bid farewell to Mr. Oliver and his dog. They left the exam room with a little frivolity in their steps.

Next was Sinbad. Throughout the suture removal on Last Chance, I could hear Sinbad's bad temperament coming to the surface in the reception area. There is no breed of cat that meows like a Siamese. With them the noise is deep, guttural, and annoying. And they have stamina with their meow. They can do it all day long if necessary for their purposes. People either like Siamese cats or they don't. There doesn't seem to be much middle ground. I had had

Siamese cats for a number of years, so I was one of those who could tolerate their cantankerous behavior. Even so, I thought the song in the movie *Lady and the Tramp* put it perfectly: "We are Siamese if you please. We are Siamese if you don't please." That's just the way they are. "You have to love them," I thought. Sinbad tested that love for the breed to the limit. Fortunately, I had the foresight to close his skin incision with a surgical adhesive. That way, I could look at him from a safe distance, ask a few questions like, "Is he eating well?" and "Has his activity level returned to normal?" and other similar questions that would have to substitute for a hands-on exam. Mr. Powell assured me that Sinbad was back to his mean and cantankerous self. The rodent population was bracing itself for some displaced anger.

This morning had also brought Mrs. Galloway and Barney to the office for his one-month recheck visit and a radiograph. Barney looked great! He stood proud like a show dog and inhaled and exhaled as if there had never been a problem. Everything looked so well on his physical exam that I was almost afraid to take the x-ray for fear that I might be disappointed for some unexplainable reason. When we placed Barney on his side this time, there was no struggling and his breathing was not labored. The x-ray of the chest looked wonderful. I had lost sleep early after Barney's surgery fearing the suture line in the diaphragm might not hold or that I may have compromised the blood supply to the abdominal muscle that I had improvised into new duty as a breathing muscle. To my complete joy, Barney's recovery from surgery had been nothing less than miraculous. I have always been amazed by the body's ability to heal and adjust to drastic challenges. Barney had reinvigorated that wonderment.

As I walked Mrs. Galloway to the door and said good-bye, my eyes were captured by a pine cone wreath on the exit door. I hadn't seen it this morning when I came through the waiting room and wondered how I could have missed such a beautiful decoration. I made a quick survey of the area and saw holly leaves with their red berries intermixed with Christmas tree balls and tinsel adorning the reception desk. Sprayed snow framed the windows and colored Christmas lights were blinking on a small Christmas tree at the opposite end of the reception room. Susan was sitting behind the reception desk wearing a Santa Claus hat and a big smile. "How do you like it?"

"Amazing! When did all this happen?"

"I had it all planned, so it didn't take but an hour to put up. While you and Alma were seeing all the rechecks this morning, I put it together. It makes our office look festive, don't you think?"

132

"It looks wonderful, Susan. Gosh, you even decorated the bulletin board." The board was covered with Christmas cards sent to us by clients. They surrounded a poem entitled "The Real Meaning of Christmas."

"Well, I hope this puts you in the spirit to go Christmas shopping. You had mentioned how behind you were on shopping for everyone's gifts so I cleared the schedule for you this morning so you could catch up. After all, Christmas is just seven days from now."

"A week from now is Christmas?"

"That's right, so you best get out of here and get busy. I'll beep you if anything important happens here."

I went through the kennel area to the back door. Alma was sitting on the floor with three little mixed breed puppies. There were tears in her eyes. She noticed me looking at her. "Don't mind me. I knew this day was coming and I'm really happy about it. Really. But after hand feeding these little guys around the clock for the past three weeks, it's hard to part with them. You know, they didn't even have their eyes open when they were abandoned at the clinic's door. Now look at them. They're into everything. But, it's for the best. We have found homes for all of them and it's time for them to move on." Alma wiped the tears from her eyes. "There're some happy tears mixed in here, too."

"You did a wonderful thing, Alma. One of those 'behind the scene things' that most people never know. I'm sure you received another jewel for your heavenly crown."

Alma smiled and picked up one of the pups and wiped some mess off its rear end. "This is one part that I won't miss," she laughed.

As I left the office I was reminded of what Susan had said. She was right. I was running short on time. Actually, I was further ahead of schedule than usual. I had ordered Linda a winter hiking coat which had already arrived, was wrapped and under the tree. Gifts for the boys were always easy. Like most parents, we would give each of them one special gift and then a bunch of little things, too. Travis's Mini Mites football uniform was already wrapped and under the tree. I had in mind that I would give Keith and Wyatt a fish tackle box stocked with an assortment of hooks, artificial bait, line, corks and the like. Harris Hardware on West Main Street would be the perfect place to find these items. The store is just a half block from the barbershop in downtown Brevard. As I drove through town, I saw Arnold McCall, Bill Larenby and CJ in front of the shop. Arnold and Bill looked a little down in the dumps so I pulled over to see how they were doing.

As I approached the three, I could see they were not in their usual exuberant moods. Arnold and Bill were sitting on the sidewalk bench with their hands stuffed in their pockets and their legs crossed. CJ was leaning against a utility pole twirling his fingers through his handlebar mustache. They all seemed to be contemplative. There was no conversation going on between them. "What's going on, fellows? Y'all seem to be a bit subdued this brisk morning."

"I reckon we're licking our wounds over that confounded steer," Arnold said.

"He's doing okay, isn't he?"

"Oh, yeah, he's doing great. The 4-H Club was happy to get him," Bill said sarcastically.

"I thought you had him penned up and were feeding him grain to get him ready for the dinner table."

"We penned him up all right, but that's about as far as we got," Arnold continued. "Bill and I brought our wives and children to see the steer. They wanted to see him since he had become somewhat of an animal-type Houdini, always eluding us and all. So we brought them over. That was a big mistake."

"Why's that?" I asked.

Bill interjected. "Guess what the first words were from their mouths?"

"I don't know. Maybe, 'Congratulations,' or something like that."

"No." He looked at CJ as to cast blame. "The very first words, I mean the very first words were, 'Is that Wooley?' My wife started talking about what a good-looking animal he was and how it seemed almost a shame that he would have to be sent to the butcher soon. Except she didn't use the word butcher. She thought she would disguise it by saying abattoir so the kids wouldn't catch on. You know, Doc, Bill Jr. and Gus are only eight and six years old, but there was no slipping that bit of information by them. Then she put the icing on the cake. She looked at Wooley's eyes. Those big brown eyes. Of course, I'd never noticed that steers had eyelashes, but she did. She pointed out how long and graceful they were and how they accented his face. Then Gus looked up at me and said, 'If that's where meat comes from, I don't want any.' Then Bill Jr. said, 'We can't eat Wooley, it's just not right.' A few weeks ago when I came home with my arm in a sling after trying to catch Wooley, I was the household hero. My image got tarnished a bit when the boys saw the steer caught up in the pen."

Arnold was next. "All I can say is ditto for my wife, except that she pointed out how shiny and bright Wooley's hair coat was. The ladies didn't say much more. They didn't have to. They just gathered the kids and left. I don't know where they think steaks come from, but one thing's for sure, their steaks weren't coming from Wooley."

"How about you, CJ?" I asked.

"You know I saved Wooley from drowning. He would surely have turned upside down with his hooves pointing to the sky had I not jumped into that pond."

"You did save him and under some pretty adverse conditions," I said. The other men nodded their heads in agreement.

"Did you ever see the movie, *Lawrence of Arabia*?" CJ said without waiting for an answer as he paced back and forth in front of the bench. "Well, there was a scene in there where Lawrence saved a man who had fallen off his camel when they were crossing a long stretch of desert. They discovered the man was missing and then Lawrence went back into the desert and rescued him."

"So?" I couldn't quite see where this illustration was going.

"Later in the story, Lawrence had to shoot the man because of some crime he committed. He had to kill the one he had saved. Every time I saw that movie, I swore to myself I would never do what Lawrence did... somehow, I never figured it would involve a steer."

"Personally, I think you men acted admirably. You had to make a tough decision. There was money riding on the line. You had cared for him, fed him, endured injuries because of him and yet when things didn't work out exactly as you planned them, you respected your family's feelings. And, CJ, you honored your conviction. On top of all that, the 4-H Club now has a fine steer for their students. It looks like this is a win-win situation for everyone. You couldn't have planned it better. And besides all that, the grocery stores never seem to have a shortage of steaks when you get a hankering for one."

"We never thought about it that way, Doc. Thanks," Arnold said.

"Bill, I bet if you take your boys to the 4-H show in the spring you will get back your hero stripes," I said with a smile. I wished the men a Merry Christmas and walked down the street to the hardware store.

When I got to the store, I was glad I had walked the short distance rather than driving the truck down there. There wasn't a parking place anywhere around. In fact, the store was unusually packed with many others who were also trying to complete their holiday

135

shopping. There were many familiar faces. I was in a casual conversation with a farm client when I saw Clarence Owenby from the corner of my eye. He was straining to check the price on a cordless drill located on a high shelf. With his head and neck out of alignment to his body by a factor of at least ninety degrees, Clarence would never be able to see the price much less reach the object. His neck was in all sorts of contortions as he struggled to get to the drill. I made my way to him through the myriad of people and lifted the tool off the shelf. I handed the tool to him as a way of getting into a conversation, I asked, "Clarence, did you ever get another cow?"

"What's that? You'll have to speak up a little."

I had forgotten how severe his deafness was and was a little reluctant to continue this type conversation in such a crowded place. However, his sparkling eyes invited my question again. When I repeated my question, I shouted at the top of my voice. The entire crowd of people, at least fifty or more, stopped their shopping and turned our way.

"Do you remember when I found that Rosie had a terminal illness and there was nothing anyone could do? After she died, did you get yourself another cow?"

"Died? Rosie didn't die," he shouted. **"She's a-doing just fine."**

I was shocked. **"But she was collapsed and on her way out when I left."**

"That's right, but all she needed was a bumpy ride. I rigged up a sling and pulled her onto the trailer with the tractor and then took her on that old trail behind the barn. I could tell half way through the ride that her eyes were brighter. When we finished, she jumped from the trailer like bees a-going after honey and she's been all right ever since."

All the shoppers were still tuned in. It was hard to shop with two grown men yelling to each other. I was taken back and didn't know exactly what to say; certainly I couldn't say anything about how bad my prognosis had been so I shouted out,

"Well, it's a shame she lost the calf. I bet it would have been a beauty."

"Oh, she had the calf, all right, and it was a sight to behold. Just nursing up a storm now. That's the reason I'm getting this drill. Need to enlarge the stalls a bit, you know."

Clarence seemed to straighten out the crook in his neck as he talked and I felt like crawling into a hole. All the customers in the store were smiling. Some of them knew Clarence and how important the cow was to him. The others quickly saw his contentment and were happy for him. They all seemed to join in his joy like a choir coming together in song. Norman Rockwell would have loved painting that picture. After the shock, I found myself smiling, even laughing. The man and his cow hadn't parted... they were to share another Christmas.